BEARDMORE
BUILT

BEARDMORE

BUILT

THE RISE AND FALL OF A CLYDESIDE SHIPYARD

Ian Johnston

Clydebank District Libraries & Museums Department
1993

Previous page. Two locomotives and the liner Cameronia at Dalmuir in late 1920. To the left the 4-4-0, no 355, of the Glasgow & South Western Railway was first built in 1895 and rebuilt by Beardmore at Dalmuir in September 1920. The 4-6-0 no 1550 was built at Dalmuir for the Great Eastern Railway. The Anchor liner Cameronia was not completed until March 1921 after having sailed to Cherbourg for completion following a strike of joiners.

ISBN 0 906938 08 2 (Cased edition)
      0 906938 05 8 (Softback edition)

First published 1993 by Clydebank District Libraries & Museums Department

Printed by Cordfall Ltd., 041 332 4640

The battleship Ramillies under the gantry on 12 October 1916 - the day of her launch. Subject to building delays, the opportunity was taken to fit anti-torpedo bulges to the ship as she lay on the stocks. This allowed for a clearance of only 1.75 feet between the hull and the pillars of the gantry. Unfortunately, Ramillies hit the bottom during her launching run.

ACKNOWLEDGEMENTS

The author is indebted to many individuals for the kind assistance and encouragement shown throughout the preparation of this manuscript. In particular I would like to mention two former Beardmore employees – the late Jim Mowat who started his working life as a hammer boy at Parkhead Forge and eventually became the Company's technical director and Mark Hope, who began an apprenticeship as a pattern maker at Dalmuir in 1922. Mark has the clearest recollection of the shipyard as a result of being sent on errands to every department – no mean feat in a shipyard one and a quarter miles long. Both men took great pride in working for Beardmore and were able to add a dimension to the Company which archival records alone cannot do.

The following individuals and organisations require special mention for their help. Michael Moss, Alma Topen and Vanna Skelly, University of Glasgow Archives. John Hood, Clydebank District Libraries & Museums Department. The staff of the Mitchell Library, Glasgow and Strathclyde Regional Archives.

The following people who worked at Dalmuir shipyard or the rather better known shipyard next door; Jimmy Black, Jack Hinshaw, Willie Luke, Joe Boyd and John Hunter. For recollections of the airship works at Inchinnan, Arthur Tannahill and Wilson Holland.

For reading the manuscript and offering advice and encouragement: Michael Moss, Dr John Brown, Brian Newman, Dr Ian Buxton, Professor Anthony Slaven, Joe Clark, John Hood, Pat Malcolm and Mary Land. For advice on specific activities, Philip Jarrett and Dugald Cameron (aviation), Hamish Stevenson and Murdoch Nicholson (locomotives). For assistance with the ship list, John Raper. The Duke of Montrose for access to his grandfathers papers; Alasdair Gregor at Clydebank District Council; Mary Campbell, daughter-in-law of A J Campbell; Irving Hyman; John Stewart and Fraser Ross and Bill Doig. Lastly I would like to thank my family for their support during many hours, weeks and months in which I was lost in the attic.

The photographs are mostly from the Beardmore collection held by University of Glasgow Archives although some are by courtesy of the Imperial War Museum, the National Maritime Museum, the Glasgow Herald, Clydebank Libraries and Museum Department, the Royal Scottish Museum, Canadian Pacific and the authors own collection. Maps, drawings and book design by the author.   Ian Johnston 1993

Works crest from the cover of the booklet commemorating the visit of King George V in 1914

Contents

Maps, Diagrams and Drawings

PREFACE

By the turn of the twentieth century, Clydeside was long established as the greatest shipbuilding river in the world. At that time there were over thirty seven different yards on the river stretching from Glasgow to Greenock. By 1913, the record year of output, the physical expansion of the industry along the banks of the Clyde was all but complete with very few new yards remaining to be built on vacant sites.

With a distinct trend towards the building of bigger and better shipyards, inevitably, one of the last few to be laid-out was the largest and best equipped of all. This was the Naval Construction Works at Dalmuir built for William Beardmore and Company.

June 1906 marked the official opening of this yard with the launching of the Lord Nelson class battleship *Agamemnon* for the Admiralty – a significant enough event for any established shipyard but something of a celebration for one which had never built a ship before. Yet only twenty four years later, when the shipbuilding industry in Britain had begun a slow decline, the gates of this shipyard were closed for the last time. The equipment and plant were sold or dismantled under the rather dramatic provision written into the sale of the yard that no ship could be built there for a period of twenty five years.

There are many reasons which make this yard especially interesting if not unique in the history of shipbuilding on the Clyde. However, before considering these, it should be said at the outset that this interest is not the obvious attraction of success measured in output, nor the fame of ships built there, nor yet in commercial success, for on all counts other shipyards fared better. Many factors combine to make this shipyard an untypical establishment – the sheer scale of the facility, the personality of its creator William Beardmore, the great diversity of manufactures and the nature of closure following chronic financial difficulties.

The bold concept which lay behind the origin of the yard was as impressive in its entrepreneurial certainty as was its size. Simply stated, this was to build a shipyard capable of turning out the largest and highest class of ship, naval or mercantile, then foreseen. This objective was to be achieved by the utilisation of the most modern facilities and the application of the most efficient building methods then available.

The remarkably varied output, possibly unequalled by any other single works in Britain,

William Beardmore 1856 - 1936, from an illustration first printed in Playfair magazine.

ranged from battleships and flying boats to locomotives and airships. While much of this diversity of output was in response to existing demand, or created by the necessity of war, William Beardmore tried hard to stimulate new demand by innovation, particularly in the fields of aviation and marine engineering. As early as 1912 for example, the Company had interested the Admiralty in proposals for a Hydroplane Carrier – the precursor of the Aircraft Carrier, which although not realised, demonstrates William Beardmore's preoccupation and fascination with novel ideas. Born in London in 1856, William Beardmore was nevertheless essentially a product of the West of Scotland. Educated at Ayr Academy and then at Glasgow High School, he was apprenticed into the family-owned Parkhead Forge in Glasgow at the age of fourteen. Later, studies in metallurgy and chemistry in London added a scientific dimension to the young Beardmore's interest in steel making.

By the turn of the century, when his new shipyard on Clydeside was being planned,

Beardmore was 44 years of age with the successful and expanding Parkhead Forge under his sole control. Sometimes described as an 'experimenter', William Beardmore took undeniable delight in the *materiél* of engineering and derived much satisfaction from applying the resources of his Company to the problems of the day. The impression is gained that everything he became involved with had to be on a grand scale and in this his Naval Construction Works at Dalmuir were wholly characteristic.

The development of the heavy armaments companies like Beardmore, Vickers and Armstrong in the early twentieth century, owed much if not everything to the Royal Navy's requirement for warships and in particular, after 1906, to the revolutionary battleship *Dreadnought*. At a stroke this ship relegated all existing battleships to the second rank and obliged the Royal Navy, determined to maintain an overwhelming superiority over other fleets, to create a dreadnought fleet from nothing. The opportunity thus presented to the armaments firms was unparalleled and much of the heavy plant laid down by these firms and indeed the entire Naval Construction Works at Dalmuir, was dedicated to the building, arming and armouring of battleships.

The austerity of the 1920s left Beardmore's armaments-centred empire high and dry, as the political desire to support continued defence spending in the aftermath of the First World War, understandably receded. Firms like Beardmore, which Governments had encouraged before and during the war, haemorrhaged dramatically as the depressed years of the twenties offered little succour to Company attempts at diversification into peacetime manufactures.

In twenty five years of existence, Dalmuir shipyard straddled the peak years of British maritime prestige and Clydeside's shipbuilding industry as well as marking, in closure, the beginning of a slow decline. Conceived as the last word in shipbuilding practice with an excellent location, superb level of equipment and facilities, the yard contributed fully to the industry on Clydeside before and during the First World War.

The closure of Beardmore's great yard in 1930 after a relatively brief working life says as much about the fickle impermanence of human activity no matter how sound, well meant or well built as it does about dismal financial performance. The extent of the personal tragedy for William Beardmore following removal from the board of his industrial empire can only be guessed at. No matter how compelling the task of restructuring the company, it must nevertheless have been difficult to witness the closure of his great shipyard which had so recently proved itself of inestimable value to the country during the First World War.

On a more practical level, the problems which beset the Company when planning the shipyard in 1900 were straight forward. The creation of major works in the midst of a rural community, imposed severe demands on the scant services and facilities which were to hand. In recognition of this, the Company erected many of the tenements needed to house some of the many thousands of people who came to work in their shipyard. The growing town of Clydebank, of which Dalmuir is a part, responded and an infrastructure of new roads, schools and shops grew around the yard. In time, Dalmuir like other industrialised parts of Britain, became a company town totally identified with the shipyard and its manufactures as it did with the less favourable realities of shipbuilding – the hardship of layoffs, short time working and finally closure. Whatever the drawbacks of being a company town were, there was nevertheless a clearly defined purpose as well as a sense of urgency about the yard and its productions. In this shipyard's close association with the naval shipbuilding programme in the years leading up to and including the First World War, the aspirations of the local community were tied to the fortunes of the yard and, thus combined, were lifted to a level of national importance before being lost in the years after closure in 1930.

This history has been written on the basis of such information as is available from the records of William Beardmore and Co Ltd held at the University of Glasgow. Apart from minute books and accounts covering all the Beardmore factories and works of which Dalmuir was only one, records and documents relating to the operation of the shipyard have not survived the years since closure. Some records relating to the shipyard were lost during the Clydebank Blitz of 1941 when the main office at Dalmuir was destroyed. Very few photographs, which surely must have been taken on a regular basis, have survived to illustrate the remarkable diversity of work undertaken at Dalmuir.

NAVAL CONSTRUCTION WORKS

By the end of the nineteenth century the Parkhead Forge in Glasgow, under the control of William Beardmore, was established as one of the most important centres in the United Kingdom for the production of heavy forgings and armour plate. The Forge had originally been set-up in 1837 and until 1860 was largely associated with the work of the pre-eminent Clydeside engineer and shipbuilder, Robert Napier. In 1860 William Rigby in partnership with William Beardmore senior, acquired and operated the works until Rigby's death in 1863. Beardmore senior, now in partnership with his brother Isaac, carried on the business until his death in 1877, whereupon his son William stepped into his father's position. By 1887 Isaac had retired and control passed exclusively into William Beardmore's hands. Throughout this period the Forge had been growing steadily and with the young William Beardmore, further substantial additions to plant and processes were made including, significantly, the start of steel armour plate manufacture in 1890.

In 1900, Robert Napier's ailing shipyard at Govan on the Clyde – famous as the birthplace of iron shipbuilding – was acquired by Beardmore, providing him with a secure outlet for the marine products of the Forge at Parkhead. There is little doubt however, that Napier's shipyard and associated engine works further up river at Lancefield Quay, were of little more than short term concern to Beardmore whose interest in naval shipbuilding would soon render the modest size of the Govan shipyard inadequate. In making this acquisition however, Beardmore was doing little more than following current trends in which several prominent steel making companies had acquired shipbuilding capacity as a means of securing and expanding their production. The most recent example of this was the take-over, in 1899, of the long established Clydebank shipyard of J and G Thomson by John Brown and Company, the Sheffield steel makers and forge masters. Ample incentive for the vertical integration of steelmaking and shipbuilding firms lay in the great size and requirements of the Royal Navy and the British merchant marine.

The jewel in naval shipbuilding was undoubtedly the battleship, the most powerful and technically advanced warship afloat. In 1900 there were over one hundred and fifty shipyards in the United Kingdom. Of these however, very few were equipped to build battleships. Traditionally, the Royal Dockyards had provided the Navy with the majority of new construction, although increasingly, and for a variety of reasons, private firms were encouraged to tender for warship orders. By the turn of the century, seven major private yards had recently built battleships for the Navy; Armstrong, Thames Iron Works, Laird, Palmers, Fairfield, John Brown and Vickers. Of these yards, two had particular advantage in the building of warships by virtue of their associated ordnance factories. Armstrong, who had amalgamated with Whitworth in 1897, had long been identified with the design and manufacture of ordnance as well as the warships to carry it. Armstrong's Elswick naval yard on Tyneside had been set up in 1884 leaving their original yard at Walker free to concentrate on the building of merchant vessels.

In 1897, Vickers steelmaking interests had been amalgamated with the ordnance firm of Maxim Nordenfelt and, thus combined, had taken over the shipyard and works of the Naval Construction and Armaments Company at Barrow-in-Furness. They now set about challenging Armstrong for leadership in the design and manufacture of ordnance as well as naval shipbuilding in Britain. Armstrong and Vickers had thereby acquired the distinct advantage of being able to build, arm and armour a warship without having to venture outside their own works except for specialist items. Together, they were the only private manufacturers of large calibre naval ordnance – a position they no doubt wished to maintain. William Beardmore's Parkhead works together with his initial proposal to build a naval shipyard and gun factory[1] on Clydeside would clearly force modification of this joint monopoly and put Beardmore in contention for a major share of new construction for the Royal Navy.

Other companies recognised the desirability of integrating gun manufacture with naval shipbuilding. The important and hitherto 'unattached' firms John Brown, Fairfield and Cammell Laird established the Coventry Ordnance Works in 1905 with the capacity to meet the complete range of naval weaponry including the manufacture of gun mountings.

Thus, a relatively small but growing number of private firms were equipped or equipping to specialise in total warship construction. Naturally, they would look to the Royal Navy as the most important, although not the only, source of orders.

For Great Britain, with her vast and disparate Empire, the navy was the means by which these interests were acquired, nurtured and protected. The Two Power Standard which became official policy in 1898, ensured that the Navy would be maintained at a size at least the equal of the combined strengths of the two largest rival fleets which were at that time France and Russia. This ensured a constant demand for new warships to replace aging and obsolete units. The procurement of new construction was achieved through the annual naval estimates presented to Parliament by the Admiralty. An influence on this process was the accelerating pace of technical development in warship design which, as a by-product, served to hasten obsolescence of existing warship types. The prime example of this occurred in 1906 with the completion of the revolutionary battleship *Dreadnought* at Portsmouth Dockyard for the Royal Navy. The appearance of this ship, which rendered all existing battleships obsolete including those in the Royal Navy, created an unprecedented opportunity for the naval yards in which Beardmore was to share.

The political factor which in time fuelled the most compelling impetus for warship construction in the very early years of this century, was the naval rivalry existing between Britain and Germany brought about largely as a result of German imperial ambitions. The 1909 naval scare focused on this issue with such intensity that orders for no less than ten dreadnought battleships and battlecruisers were placed in Britain over just one twelve month period. It was therefore against this forthcoming complex technical and political background that William Beardmore prepared to enter the potentially profitable activity of naval shipbuilding .

In January 1902, in order to raise fresh capital for the expansion of his works, Beardmore formed a limited company – William Beardmore and Company Limited – in which Vickers purchased half of the ordinary shares. Vickers' significant financial interest in the new Beardmore company appears in part to have been prompted by a desire to circumscribe the latter's attempts to manufacture ordnance thereby preserving the virtual monopoly Vickers shared with Armstrong. Both firms regarded Beardmore with considerable apprehension and Vickers tried repeatedly to encourage an Armstrong shareholding in Beardmore by means of extending control over

that company. With two seats out of five on the Beardmore board, Vickers was able to monitor the new company very closely as indeed it was in its interest, as William Beardmore was heavily in their debt.[2] The Beardmore board members were; William Beardmore, chairman and managing director; Joseph Beardmore, William's brother; The Marquis of Graham, who joined the board in January 1906; Albert Vickers and Lieutenant Trevor Dawson. The two last named were the Vickers representatives.

DALMUIR

The early development of iron shipbuilding on the upper reaches of the River Clyde had taken place relatively close to the central part of Glasgow and adjoining districts like Govan and Partick. As the Clyde grew in importance as a shipping river, quite distinct from the growth of shipbuilding, the trustees of the port began to develop facilities in the form of new wharves and graving docks. The creation of new port facilities obliged several shipbuilders to relocate their yards further down river to make way for the growing port. By the end of this period of expansion and relocation around the turn of the century, there was an almost continuous line of yards stretching from Glasgow to Clydebank, a distance of over seven miles. This process had not been entirely unhelpful to shipbuilders as it created the opportunity to lay-out modern and better equipped yards, more capable in dealing with the increasing size and sophistication of ships. However, when William Beardmore came to purchase land for his new shipyard in 1900, the only site large enough for his purposes which was reasonably close to Glasgow's labour supply as well as his own parent works, was at Dalmuir, to the west of Clydebank.[3] By this time, the available ground for shipbuilding on the upper Clyde had been all but exhausted and thereafter only three new yards were to be established on open sites.[4]

Dalmuir was a small hamlet which, in 1886, had moved one chronicler of the times to write – 'down to quite recently, there were in it only a sparse population, located here and there in a very unmethodical fashion'.[5] With the exception of a calico works, a paper mill and a soda works manufacturing sulphuric acid – all eighteenth century developments which were either closed or run down – industry, which had taken the Clyde and Glasgow by storm, had left Dalmuir Sea

high and dry. Dalmuir did, however, have one connection with the river in the form of a small marine workshop owned by the Clyde Navigation Trust which had been constructed in 1860, on the site of the former soda works, for the repair and maintenance of their fleet of dredgers, hoppers and harbour craft.[6] The existence of this workshop created a major problem in the construction of Beardmore's new shipyard as it was located literally in the middle of a large tract of land earmarked for the excavation of a very large graving dock, rightly seen by Beardmore as a valuable and important part of his shipyard scheme. However it was not until seven years later in 1907,[7] that the Clyde Trustees finally vacated the site in favour of new works up-river at Renfrew.

Between 1900 and 1901, eighty acres of land were purchased by the Beardmore Company for the new yard principally from the Dunn-Pattison and the McIndoe estates.[8] The site was ideally suited to shipbuilding by virtue of its location on a bend in the river which permitted slipways to be arranged so that an uninterrupted launching run upstream was possible regardless of ship size – a feature no other shipyard enjoyed on the upper reaches of the Clyde. In the years to follow, the narrowness of the upper part of the river restricted the size of vessels capable of being built at most yards and it was only the fortuitous position of the John Brown yard opposite the mouth of the River Cart that enabled very large ships, including the Queens, to be launched at all.

Below. An 1896 ordnance map of the Dalmuir area showing the approximate area of the Naval Construction Works which was bounded by Clydebank shipyard to the east, the Lanarkshire & Dunbartonshire Railway to the north and the Corporation of Glasgow Sewage Treatment works(built concurrently with the shipyard) to the west. The awkward location of the Clyde Navigation Trust's Workshops is easily seen.

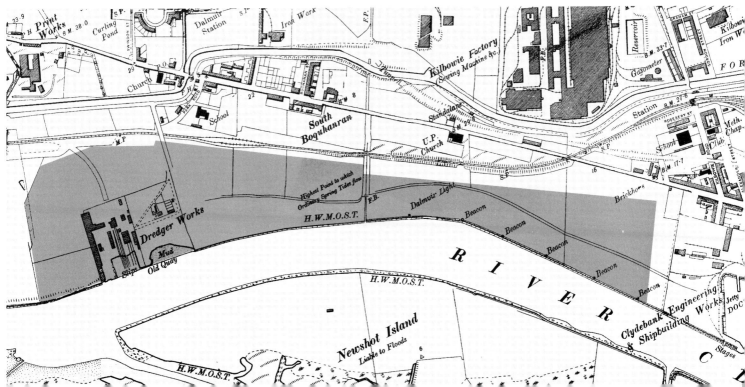

Outwith the land purchased for the new shipyard at Dalmuir, additional land was purchased nearby for the building of workers' housing. In July 1904 twenty acres were purchased from the Lanarkshire and Dunbartonshire Railway Co. for £18,500 and in January 1905, a further eight and a half acres were purchased from the Dunn-Pattison estate.[9] While it was not exceptional for large firms to provide housing for their workers the almost complete absence of existing accommodation together with difficulties in finding suitable building ground in the district, give the firm little choice in the matter. Prior to the arrival of industry, the town of Clydebank did not exist at all, the area being given over to farmland. When J and G Thomson's shipyard (later John Brown) arrived in Clydebank in 1871 followed by the American Singer Sewing Machine Company in 1882, the district underwent a period of phenomenal growth during which time the population almost quadrupled from 5,000 in 1886 to 19,080 in 1900.[10]

Very few photographs showing the building of Dalmuir shipyard exist. In this picture an unidentified foreman stands on the grillage of a column at the Engine Works during course of erection in 1904

At the planning stage of the new yard, the Beardmore Company indicated to the Burgh Council that employment would be approximately 7,000 persons.[11] However such was the pace of development, that in addition to considering the implications of a new shipyard, the Council also had to make allowances for two other major projects in the district. These were the large sewage treatment works to be built for Glasgow Corporation and the Rothesay Dock, the latest dock development for the Clyde Navigation Trust. In the light of these developments, Clydebank Burgh Council estimated that a further 10,000 to 15,000 people would be added to the population over the next 5 to 10 years.[12] The acute shortage of building land within existing boundaries prompted the council to apply for an extension to the Burgh and this was granted in 1906 in the form of a sixth ward.

If land was a problem, transport links with Glasgow and beyond were not. Two railway lines served the district, the North British Railway Company's to the north of the district completed in 1875 and the Lanarkshire and Dunbartonshire Company's completed in 1896 which ran much closer to the river. Indeed, Dalmuir Riverside Station, on the latter line, was only a few yards from the main gate of the new works. On the 10th of October 1904 communication links were further enhanced when the city of Glasgow's comprehensive tram network was extended into the centre of Dalmuir thereby enabling travel from virtually any part of the city at reasonable cost.

CONSTRUCTION OF THE WORKS

In accordance with William Beardmore's intention to create an exceptionally large and well equipped naval shipbuilding yard, the design and layout was entrusted to two senior men already in Company employment; Edmund Sharer, a native of Sunderland and recently shipyard manager at Fairfield's Govan shipyard, was employed in 1900 at Beardmore's Govan yard as General Manager, and William Walker May, the manager of Beardmore's Lancefield Engine Works.

The first phase of construction was the contract to build and excavate the new fitting-out basin and this was awarded to James Goldie and Sons of St Enochs Square, Glasgow.[13] While Goldie was setting up site offices in August 1901, an encouraging gesture and expression of official interest in the project was made when the Third Sea Lord, Admiral May, in company with the Director of Dockyards, Sir James Williamson, visited the site.[14] Work began in earnest in late 1901 with the levelling of the site and excavation of the fitting-out basin. Construction appears to have been somewhat protracted; when Beardmore leased Napier's Govan yard in 1900 it was initially for a period of two years only suggesting that the new yard would be operational by the end of 1902. Further evidence of this is supported by plans to lay down the armoured cruiser *Carnarvon* in the new yard in the Autumn of 1902.[15] These proposals had to be abandoned however because the yard was insufficiently advanced. If 1902 was rather optimistic, it was nevertheless another three years before the first vessel could be laid down and yet another one before the works were officially opened. Even by the building standards of the day, four years was a very long time to build a shipyard and the delay was almost certainly as a result of the Company's rather precarious financial position which resulted in many of the buildings being erected in 1904 and not sooner. After 1906, building work on the shipyard in the form of extensions never ceased and particularly from 1910 onwards, there was almost continuous expansion of facilities, largely in response to increasing naval demand.

The list opposite gives the principal buildings erected at Dalmuir shipyard in the period up to 1905, in approximate building order with costs where known.[16] The dates are those in which Clydebank Burgh Council granted building approval. In addition to these buildings there were numerous small stores, sheds, time offices, canteens, lavatories, a complete standard gauge railway served by two tank locomotives built by Andrew Barclay and Sons and a steel plate and section stockyard served by a 'Goliath' type travelling crane.[17] The Statement of Accounts for the year ending December 1905 records the following costs for all work carried out in connection with Dalmuir to that time.

Together with costs of £113,072 incurred during 1906 to complete the works, this gives a total in the region of over £900,830 which is approximately equivalent to £45 million today.

The development of shipbuilding on the Clyde enabled a wealth of supporting industries to develop, many of whom were involved in the manufacture of shipyard plant and facilities.

PRINCIPAL BUILDINGS ERECTED AT DALMUIR SHIPYARD		
Fitting-out basin	November 1901	£128,181 15s
150 ton Fitting-out Crane	June 1902	£21,400
Power Station	November 1902	£11,255 5s 3d
Engine & Boiler Shop	March 1903	£48,283 17s 8d
Gas Producers & Recovery Plant	April 1903	
Platers' Shed	December 1903	£9,882 8s
Joiners' Shop	February 1904	£5,624 6s 1d
Riggers Loft, Paint Shop & Boat Shed	February 1904	
Smithy & Angle Iron Smithy	April 1904	£5,383 10s 3d
General Store & Mould Loft	April 1904	£4,304 13s 2d
Admiralty Store	April 1904	£1,672 15s 8d
Mechanics & Brass Finishers Shop	June 1904	£2,743 10s 11d
Pattern Shop	July 1904	
General Offices	August 1904	
Plumbers Shop	September 1905	
Shipbuilding Gantry	October 1904	£18,780 8s 2d
Sawmill	November 1904	

COSTS AT DALMUIR SHIPYARD TO YEAR ENDING 1905	
Land	£91,548 14s 11d
Dock (fitting-out basin)	£128,181 15s
Buildings:	£188,362 4s 4d
Fixed plant and machinery	£379,667 19s 9d
TOTAL	£787,760 14s

Concentrated mostly in the Glasgow area, firms such as Craig & Donald, Bennie & Sons, Hugh Smith and Sir William Arrol acquired international reputations and exported their manufactures the world over. Perhaps the most significant of these firms was Arrol, builders of the Forth Railway Bridge and Tower Bridge in London. This remarkable firm designed and supplied all manner of industrial buildings, berth gantries and shipyard cranes. All steel framed buildings and steel structures at Dalmuir were erected by Arrol in conjunction with James Goldie and Sons who carried out all brick and foundation work.

Concurrently with the building of the shipyard, permission to construct tenements for workers was granted by the Council early in 1905. This was for a total of 37 tenements and the creation of five new roads. Each tenement block, built of red sandstone, was four stories high and usually contained two or three flats on each floor. The most commodious of these were the three built on the corner site on Dumbarton Road and the

Beardmore tenements as they are today. This block on the corner of Agamemnon Street and Dumbarton Road, was built in 1906 and intended for foremen working in the shipyard.

Below. Three stone carved details from the building above which mark the year of building,1906, a pre-dreadnought battleship similar to the Agamemnon and the company initials WB & Co Ltd. The stonework proved to be much more durable than the shipyard.

Below right. The floor plan of two adjoining tenement flats on Dumbarton Road from a drawing dated May 1906 by architects Whyte & Galloway of Bath Street Glasgow. These two-room and single-room and kitchen flats are well appointed and would have been for foremen or persons of similar position.

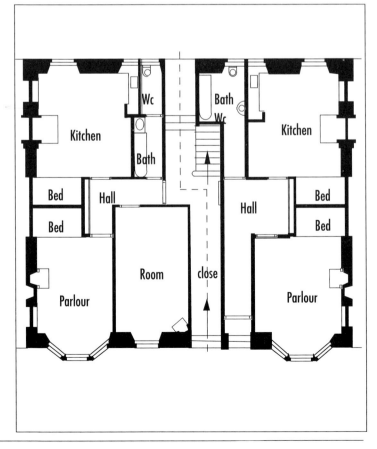

The Tower. Very large stone villas were occupied by senior management. This villa, known as The Tower, was occupied by the manager of the Engine Works.

newly formed Agamemnon Street, named after the battleship then building in the yard. These tenements were intended for occupation by shipyard foremen and contained two rooms, a kitchen and, as a newspaper report of the time expressed it, a 'light' bathroom. This meant a w.c. a wash-hand basin and a bath all with a cold water supply only. The ground floor was completed as shops with polished granite fronts. Carved out of the sandstone approximately half way up the front elevation of this handsome building was, and still is, a monogram of the Company's initials alongside a rendering of a pre-Dreadnought battleship. The remaining 34 tenements were built close to the west of the shipyard and were of the one room and kitchen type with an inside w.c. It was estimated that together, the 37 tenements would provide accommodation for 400 families or 2,000 people and that the combined value of the properties was in the region of £100,000.[18]

Between 1906 and 1907, a further 22 tenements were built in Dumbarton Road. Plans were also in hand for a further 60 tenements of the 'superior' type on the site of an old paper works close by Dumbarton Road but this development did not proceed until after the outbreak of war in 1914

when accommodation once again became a serious problem. A simple approximation based on the 59 tenements actually built by or around 1907 reveals a minimum figure of about 600 employees housed by the Company. It is almost certain that a good number of these would have been foremen or held jobs equivalent to that position. In 1907 twelve semi-detached villas were purchased for the price of £6,000 and a further six houses at Reith Place were acquired from the Clyde Trust for £1,370.[19] Housing of this sort was provided for middle management positions or persons of similar status.

The most desirable and prestigious accommodation was given to senior management who were very well paid by the standards of the day. Four of them were housed in exceptionally large stone built detached villas which had been erected in Dalmuir during the 1880s or earlier.[20] The largest of these was Melbourne House, occupied by the Works General Manager. This house which had a most imposing pillared entrance and a marble clad hallway, was extremely well appointed and had a full size tennis court in grounds to the rear. By virtue of its location on the side of a hill which gently rose away from the river,

A 1904 view of the recently completed 150 ton hammerhead crane. The large fitting-out basin has also been completed but not yet flooded. To the left, the power station and gas plant are still under construction. Some of the large detached villas subsequently occupied by shipyard management, including Melbourne House and the Tower, are just visible to the immediate right of the crane's tower.

Melbourne House commanded a watchful view of the shipyard below. All houses and flats built or purchased by the Company were no more than a short distance from the yard.

WORKS DESCRIPTION

The following description together with the plan showing the layout of the Naval Construction Works as built at Dalmuir, are intended to give some indication of what a large, well equipped shipbuilding yard looked like in the early years of the twentieth century. A brief description illustrating the function of each department or workshop in relation to the shipbuilding process is given.

Unlike some shipyards such as Harland & Wolff of Belfast who erected distinctive red brick buildings with a definite house style, the buildings and workshops erected at Dalmuir shipyard were of no particular architectural merit being merely typical, if somewhat larger examples of their type which could be found in yards and works throughout the United Kingdom.[21]

FITTING-OUT BASIN

This was claimed to be the largest fitting-out basin built for any private shipyard in the United Kingdom. It was 900 feet long, 360 feet wide and enclosed an area of 7.5 acres. It was served by the giant hammerhead crane described below.

150 TON FITTING-OUT CRANE

This crane was designed and manufactured in Germany by the Benrather Maschinenfabrik A G of Benrath near Düsseldorf.[22] Together with a similar crane at Vickers' Barrow yard, these were the first modern large capacity cranes of any type in Britain. Beardmore and Vickers reached agreement with the Benrather Company and Friedrich Siemens in January 1903 with a view to the manufacture and sale of cranes of this type in the UK.[23] The Dalmuir crane was erected by the German firm Kohncke for whom a payment of £3,352 is recorded in the accounts for 1903.

Other British shipbuilders followed soon after in the installation of giant cranes although most favoured British designed versions which differed

in principle and had a more massive appearance than their German counterparts. With their distinctive silhouettes, cranes of this type formed the classic image of heavy industry on rivers throughout the country. The primary function of this crane was to make very heavy lifts possible during the fitting-out of a vessel, including the shipping of main propelling machinery, boilers, armour, gun-mountings and other heavy concentrated loads.

The Dalmuir hammerhead crane consisted of a double armed horizontal revolving cantilevered jib connected to a crane post which went down through a quadrilateral tower to the ground. The crane post turned on two bearings, one a steel pressure ring with four double rollers at the top of the tower, the other a cast steel cylindrical bearing set in masonry at the bottom. On completion, this crane was tested with a load of 200 tons at a radius

of 72 feet 2 inches on the short arm of the cantilever. The crab on the long arm, could lift 50 tons at a radius of 139 feet 5 inches. Under maximum load, the crane could lift at a rate of 5 feet per minute and it took 8 minutes to make one complete revolution of the cantilever. The crane was electrically driven with two 52 bhp motors on each crab for hoisting, one 18 bhp motor for slewing, and two 14 bhp motors for racking. All electrical equipment was manufactured by Union Electrizitätsgesellschaft of Berlin.[24]

The main cantilever was 233 feet long and the height to the trolley rail on top of this girder was 154 feet. Communication to the cranesman's cabin aloft was by voice tube. The crane's structure weighed over 500 tons.

POWER STATION
As the entire works were to be 'activated' by

The German designed and built hammerhead crane towers over the battleship Agamemnon *during fitting-out in late 1906. Work is in progress fitting the armoured belt to the ship's side the recesses for which can be clearly seen. To the left, the ship's funnel, always completed before fitting onboard, is under construction.*

Most views of the shipyard in this chapter were taken during 1906 unless otherwise stated.

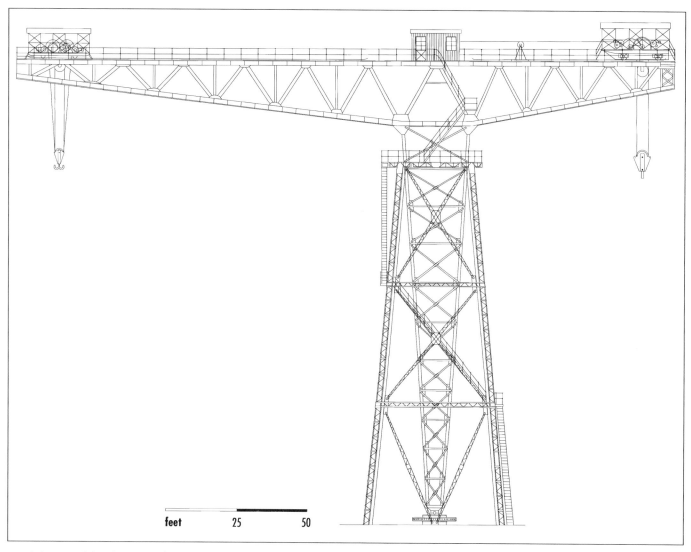

feet　　　25　　　50

A drawing of the 150 ton Benrather crane. This crane was the first of its type on Clydeside and, together with subsequent cranes of this type, became synonymous with the image of heavy industry in this country.

electricity, still something of a novelty, the Company followed normal practice by building their own power station to supply electricity, compressed air and gas to the various shipyard and engine departments throughout the yard. As originally built, the power station housed four Oechelhauser gas engines capable of developing 4,000 bhp and generating 2,750 kW of electricity. Two additional gas engines, each of 400 bhp, drove air compressors each of which could supply pneumatic tools at the rate of 1,200 cubic feet per minute at a pressure of 100 lb per square inch. The compressors were supplied by Alley & MacLellan and the gas engines (under license to the Oechelhauser Company) were manufactured by Duncan Stewart Ltd of Glasgow. Both of these firms were part of the Beardmore group of companies having been acquired earlier.

Gas to drive the gas engines was made from coal in the Producer Plant adjacent to the Power Station building. This plant also supplied gas for combustion to the various furnaces in the Engine Works, Platers' shed and other smithies, through 3 foot diameter steel pipes which traversed the works supported by steel pylons at a height of 30 feet.

The choice of gas producers and engines as the principal source of power generation, was made by William Beardmore personally following a tour of various generating systems on the continent to evaluate their effectiveness.[25] The attractiveness of this system lay in its very low cost, as the price of the coal required to initiate the process was considerably offset by the installation of Duff ammonia recovery plant which produced saleable waste products such as tar, creosote and ammonia

Above. The power station and gas producers nearing completion in 1905. In the foreground, the foundations have been prepared for a furnace and other small buildings. Soon after completion, the power station was extended and more gas engines added as the original plant was not able to meet actual needs.

Left. The Oechelhauser gas engines in the power station installed to generate all electrical and compressed air requirements

Above. Engine shop No 2 bay. In the background light machining of small components is in progress whilst in the foreground, detailed hand fitting and sub-assembly takes place.

Engine Shop smithy showing a number of pneumatic hammers of varying capacities down the centre and small gas fired hearths to either side.

sulphate. Less than two years after completion, the power station was found to be unable to meet the full demand for power and the building was extended by 50 feet to accommodate an additional gas engine of 2,000 bhp. Likewise, the five original gas producers installed, were extended to a total of seven over the next few years.

ENGINE AND BOILER SHOP

The dimensions of this shop, which covered an area of 5.5 acres, made it one of the largest of its type in the United Kingdom. It was constructed by Sir William Arrol and Company pioneers of steel framed, steel clad industrial buildings with glazed roofs in contrast to the hitherto standard brick structure.[26]

The shop contained five bays all of which ran the full length of 720 feet. Two of these bays were 80 feet wide and rose 65 feet to the underside of the roof girders. The Boiler Shop occupied the

northern half of the building, the Engine Shop the southern half. Inside, the shops were equipped to a level commensurate with the great size of the building. The Boiler Shop was equipped to deal with boiler plates up to 38 feet long by 12.5 feet wide and two inches thick. Boiler riveting machines were installed capable of riveting boilers of any foreseen diameter up to 24 feet long. These machines applied a closing pressure of 200 tons on rivets. In the Boiler Shop Smithy, plates of 20 feet diameter could be worked on the flanging machines. Pneumatic hammers ranged in size up to 30 cwts. Gas for the smithy fires as well as compressed air for the pneumatic hammers was supplied by the Power Station. Machinery was installed for the manufacture of large, and later small tube boilers.

Like the Boiler Shop, the Engine Shop was similarly equipped with machinery of the largest dimensions capable of manufacturing

The great size of the boiler shops are evident in this view of No 5 bay showing a 34 foot by 12 foot boiler shell plate for the ss Quillota being curved in the bending rolls. To the right, corrugated boiler furnaces await assembly into Scotch boilers such as those in the background.

The Boiler Shop smithy showing boiler end plates being flanged and a series of column mounted hydraulic radial cranes of 4 tons capacity. The earth floor is typical of most smithy shops.

Opposite top. A series of plates being marked out with white paint for punching on the 'boards' of the platers shed. A combination punching and shearing machine can be seen to the left. The absence of overhead cranes indicates continuing reliance on manual labour.

The Brass Finishers Shop. Most machines at Dalmuir were independently powered, but here line shafting from wall mounted motors drives several vertical drills. Note the large lathe to the left, the row of bench vices to the right and the sandstone grinder in centre background.

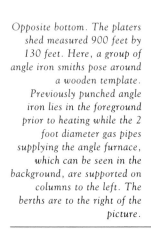

Opposite bottom. The platers shed measured 900 feet by 130 feet. Here, a group of angle iron smiths pose around a wooden template. Previously punched angle iron lies in the foreground prior to heating while the 2 foot diameter gas pipes supplying the angle furnace, which can be seen in the background, are supported on columns to the left. The berths are to the right of the picture.

reciprocating machinery of the largest size. The biggest of the lathes had beds 100 feet in length with 120 inch headstocks. Planing machines could handle work up to 26 feet by 18 feet. A gallery was constructed over number three bay where brass fittings and components were machined. Overhead cranage provided lifts of from 10 tons to 60 tons per crane; 120 tons was possible if two 60 ton cranes were yoked together. Equipped initially for the manufacture of reciprocating machinery, the Engine works were later tooled for turbine manufacture and, after the end of the First World War, for the cutting of reduction gearing.

All material for the Engine and Boiler Shops was carried by rail into the mid-point of the shop and then taken to whichever side it was required. On completion, engines and boilers were taken on low loaders from exit points at either end of the shop to the dockside for installation by the giant hammerhead crane.

PLATERS SHED
The Platers Shed was positioned along the head of the berths and measured 900 feet long by 130 feet

The Sawmill measured 300 x 120 feet. Logs were brought from the log pond by overhead crane and placed on the log saws seen here.

wide. The plate rolling machines and plate edge planers, capable of handling plates 40 feet long by 7.5 feet wide and 2 inches thick, were supplied by Bennie & Sons of Glasgow. In 1905 these machines were claimed to be the largest in use anywhere. The centre section of the Platers' Shed was equipped with gas fired plate and angle furnaces which were 50 and 80 feet long respectively. There were numerous punching and shearing machines supplied by Craig & Donald of Johnstone. Material from the nearby plate and angle stockyards, was transported by a travelling 'Goliath' crane with a maximum lift of 5 tons at a radius of 120 feet.

SAWMILL
Timber for use in the yard was towed up-river from the log ponds at West Ferry and Langbank opposite Dumbarton, and kept in the yard's own log pond adjacent to the sawmill. When required, the logs

were lifted by an overhead crane running on a gantry which delivered the logs directly onto the cradles of the log saw. Here they were ripped into planks of various thicknesses. The timber was then placed in open sided sheds behind the sawmill and, to prevent endsplitting, the ends were painted with 'red lead' or 'smudge'. The planks were turned occasionally to prevent warping and winding. The normal time taken for air drying was two inches for every year. Steam kiln drying, which was much quicker, was undertaken at a second sawmill beside the Joiners' Shop.

JOINERS SHOP
This shop contained working areas for joiners, cabinet makers, polishers and carpenters, the latter also known as shipwrights. Joiners considered themselves to be the more skilled of the two and it was they who carried out much of the fitting-out work on board ship including cabins, wheelhouses

etc. Shipwrights made all deck fittings – hatch covers, hand rails etc. and also caulked the deck. They were also responsible for preparing and lining up ships' frames on the building berth as well as the shoring and preparation of launch ways. The making of ships' furniture, chart tables and other fittings was carried out by cabinet makers who were regarded as the most skilled of all the woodworkers.

The upper floor of the Joiners Shop was arranged in the form of a gallery, leaving a well in the centre of the shop through which natural light from the glazed roof could pass to the ground floor where the cabinetmakers worked. The gallery provided space for the patternmakers, french polishers, wood carvers and turners. The Model Making section, where display models of ships under construction in the yard were made, was also located in the Joiners Shop.

Sawdust and shavings from the woodworking appliances were carried away by an extractor system through ducts to be burnt in the furnace where steam was generated to heat the timber drying store. An impressive sprinkler system was employed throughout this shop which provided one nozzle for every ten square feet of working space. This system was pressurised by a 12,000 gallon water tank located in a 70 foot high tower at the corner of the building. The Joiners shop also housed the works horse-drawn fire tender and fire station.

RIGGERS LOFT AND BOAT SHED
Normally the entire complement of ship's lifeboats was built in the yard by boat builders in the Boat Shed. The upper floor of this building was occupied by the riggers. Riggers were responsible for the fitting of all ropes, hemp or wire, used throughout the ship in their various forms; rigging, mooring ropes, hawsers etc. They also

The Joiners Shop which also included cabinetmakers and polishers. A number of deck houses, skylights and items of furniture can be seen. Note the natural light from the glazed central well.

Above. The Pattern Makers Shop measured 200 x 50 feet. The racks in the gallery above were used for storing patterns likely to be used again.

Below. The General Office seen from the fitting-out basin. The main gas pipe and power cables leading from the power station to the platers shed and elsewhere can be seen.

in these shops were pneumatic while the furnaces were fired by gas from the gas plant, the blast being provided from compressors housed in the shop.

GENERAL STORE AND MOULD LOFT
The General Store was the repository for the multitude of items required by the various trades such as hand held drilling machines, caulking machines and riveting machines etc. The Mould Loft, 300 feet long, was located on the floor above the General Store. Here the ships' lines were marked off full scale and light wooden templates made, where appropriate, for transferring to the Platers Shed or elsewhere in the yard.

ADMIRALTY STORE
As the class of work on Admiralty contracts was of a higher standard than that of merchant work, distinction between the two was made throughout the various shops in the yard. Thus the Admiralty Store was used for material and equipment destined for warships, e.g. range finders, small calibre ordnance, searchlights etc.

MECHANICS AND BRASS FINISHERS SHOP
In the Mechanics Shop, engineers made a variety of fittings from davits to steering gear. Brass castings from the foundry – portholes, valves, seacocks etc, were completed to specification in the Brass Finishers Shop.

prepared slings for lifting objects on board ships fitting-out. The works fire engine was manned by riggers.

PAINT SHOP
This shop was used as a base and material store, by painters, red-leaders and glazers.

BLACKSMITHS AND ANGLE IRON SMITHS SHOP
The blacksmiths carried out all heavier forgings ranging from handrails and stanchions to davits. The angle iron smiths formed the light angles used in fixing bulkheads to decks etc. The hammers

Above. The 300 x 70 foot wide Mould Loft showing a full scale template laid out on the floor.

Left. The Engine Drawing Office. Nobody sat in those days.

Opposite. The stone portico of the entrance to the General Office. The stone carving is of a pre-Dreadnought type battleship.

PATTERN SHOP

Parts of engines such as cylinder heads, turbine casings, sole plates, columns etc, which had to be cast, required to have wooden patterns made first. This task was performed by pattern makers – skilled woodworkers. All patterns except those for brass casting were sent outside the yard for casting. On return, the patterns were kept in the Pattern Store should re-use prove necessary. The shipyard Pattern Shop, where patterns for hawse-pipes, bollards etc, were made, was located in the Joiners Shop.

GENERAL OFFICE

Known as the 'Naval Construction Office', this three storey building housed management, clerical and wages staff as well as the drawing offices. One half of the ground floor was occupied by separate shipyard and engine works counting houses, safes and small staff rooms. The other half was given over to the General Managers office and adjoining private luncheon room both of which had a large bay window overlooking the fitting-out basin. Close to this was a second and larger luncheon room and a large model room. There were four separate drawing offices on the first floor the two largest being the engine drawing office and the ship drawing office. Two smaller offices both designated 'private drawing office' were used for boiler and Admiralty work. Adjacent to the drawing offices was a large tracing office and small offices for the chief draughtsmen and the chief 'lady' tracer. Print rooms and darkrooms occupied the top floor. The basement was divided into a number of small rooms for use by overseers, a room designated the 'hospital', a garage for the works ambulance and a wine cellar.

The General Office, although a fairly

The ship drawing office. All hull and superstructure drawings were hand drawn before copying by tracers. There are a series of wooden half hulls fixed to the partition to the left.

nondescript brick built building, had an imposing stone entrance with pillars capped by a pediment.

PLUMBERS AND SHEET IRON SHOP

All pipes needed throughout a ship were formed to the required shape and flanged in the Plumbers' Shop. The pipes were sent outside the works for galvanising before final installation in the ship. The distinction between steel and copper pipes was observed in 1912 when a separate Copper Shop was built. The Sheet Iron Shop dealt with steel plate of 10 Standard Wire Gauge up to about .25 of an inch thick and included the making of heating and ventilation trunking, electrical ducts and lockers. Steel of lighter gauge was worked by sheet metal workers.

BRASS FOUNDRY

This was the only foundry in the works, all other casting being sent out. The Brass Foundry was housed in one of the buildings previously erected by the Clyde Trust Workshops. Most of the other Clyde Trust buildings inherited in 1907 were subsequently demolished.

THE SHIPBUILDING BERTHS

As originally laid-out, piling was completed for a total of six berths, two of which could accommodate vessels 1,000 feet long by 100 feet in breadth. Number 2 berth was fitted with an overhead shipbuilding gantry. The berths to either side of the gantry were initially equipped with light pole derricks and steam winches which could be repositioned as required. Before and after the First World War, these derricks were replaced with much more substantial steel lattice derricks of five tons capacity. Where loads heavier than five tons had to be fitted into a hull while still on

A magnificent view at the head of the berths taken about 1906 with a ship in frame to the right of the gantry and the platers' shed to the right of shot. Perhaps caught reluctantly between two tank locomotives, the carter is consoling his horse.

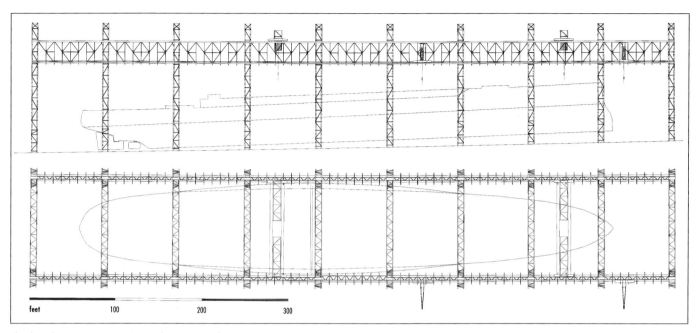

the berth, as was sometimes the case with armour plates and boilers on warships, sheer legs were stepped on the deck of the ship and so arranged that a lift could be made from the ground onto the ship and then, by moving the sheer legs, lowering the item into the appropriate space. An inventory of steel lattice derricks made when the yard closed in 1930 recalled a total of 14 of five ton capacity and 5 of three ton capacity all built by Sir William Arrol and Company.

THE SHIPBUILDING GANTRY

At the turn of the century, the most common means of handling material for erection on the building berth was the light pole derrick, held in the desired location by means of guy ropes and capable of a lift of only a few tons by using steam winches. These derricks subsequently evolved into more sophisticated steel lattice structures with a lift of up to five tons as well as motors for hoisting, racking and slewing. Derricks of this sort were first used on Clydeside in 1907 when Arrol supplied two for use on the construction of the *Lusitania* at John Brown's. These derricks still required to be held in position by a system of steel guy ropes.

In planning Dalmuir shipyard in 1901 however, the only alternative to the light pole derrick existed in the form of the shipbuilding gantry although they were extremely large, complex structures and a considerably more expensive option than derricks. Varying types of gantry were

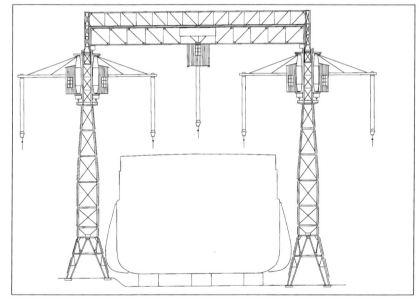

in use abroad particularly in the USA and Germany although in general, shipbuilders in Britain tended not to favour them – the only other extensive one built in Britain at that time being that of Swan Hunter and Wigham Richardson on the Tyne. In addition to a high initial cost, gantries required considerable maintenance which could prove expensive. Company accounts for 1906 recorded a figure of £102 for berth gantry and crane maintenance. Despite that, they were undoubtedly more efficient than pole derricks promising shorter berth time and certainly would have had an appeal to William Beardmore who was already committed

Side, plan and end elevations of the 755 foot long shipbuilding gantry built by Sir William Arrol in 1905.

Opposite. A view of the pre-Dreadnought battleship Agamemnon dwarfed under the massive shipbuilding gantry shortly befre her launch in June 1906.

to the adoption of the most modern facilities at Dalmuir.

By early 1903 discussions concerning the type and size of gantry to be built were underway and although Arrol was subsequently awarded the contract, at least one German firm had submitted proposals. The overall characteristics of the massive gantry erected at Dalmuir were outlined by Edmund Sharer and designed and constructed by Arrol.[27] The gantry had the following overall dimensions; 755 feet long, 150 feet high at the water's edge and 135 feet wide. The internal width between pillars and, therefore, the factor which would determine the maximum size of ship which it could accommodate, was 105 feet. As originally built, the gantry was fitted with four side walking jib cranes each capable of a five ton lift at a thirty foot outreach. These cranes were arranged in pairs on either side of the gantry facing inwards. One overhead travelling crane of fifteen tons capacity ran the length of the structure. Allowance was made for future extension to either side of the gantry and at an early stage in the building of the yard the possibility of covering 'three or four berths if not all' was considered, although not carried out.[28] Shortly after completion, four additional side walking cranes were fitted in pairs to the outside of the gantry serving the berths to either side. A second overhead travelling crane of twenty tons capacity was also added followed by a third some years later. The operation of the gantry appears to have been entirely satisfactory, although, during winds of exceptional force in January 1908, one of the two overhead cranes then fitted was blown along its tracks for a distance of 200 feet before plunging into the Clyde 130 feet below carrying both cranemen to their deaths. Prompt action on the part of the men in the other crane, which meant chaining it to the nearest girder, saved their lives.[29] Following this incident the braking systems were modified by Arrol. The Dalmuir gantry was the precursor of the larger double gantry built by Arrol at Belfast for Harland & Wolff.

Consideration was given to enclosing the entire structure but was rejected owing to the difficulty of internal lighting. A glazed roof was also rejected as, on windy days, it would tend to increase the strength of the wind through the structure.

A landmark for miles around, the shipbuilding gantry at Dalmuir represented in visual as much as in practical terms, William Beardmore's determination to build big, build well and build often. Paradoxically, so rapid was the growth in size of the battleship – the construction of which the gantry was primarily intended – that by the end of World War One, it would have been unable to accommodate the designs then under consideration. This was precisely the case in 1921 when the yard received an order to build a battlecruiser with a beam 1 foot greater than the width of the gantry.

In February 1904, Arrol quoted a price of £14,375 for a single gantry and £24,150 for a double. These prices did not include site preparation or foundations. The gantry built at

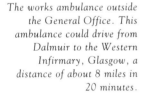

Dalmuir weighed 1,342 tons.

As completed in 1906, the shipyard was close to William Beardmore's original plan although it is likely that had the financial position of the Company been stronger, Beardmore would have continued to expand facilities at Dalmuir. Apart from the extension of the gantry, the one other major feature which was not built was a 1,000 foot long graving dock earmarked for the ground occupied by the Clyde Trust Workshops. Despite the availability of this land from 1907 onwards, the Company was in no position to finance such a major undertaking and the graving dock was never built despite the creation of a separate company – the Dalmuir Dry Dock Company – to manage it.[30] Thus the first opportunity to build a truly large graving dock on Clydeside was lost at a crucial stage in the development of shipbuilding on the river.

CONDITIONS OF EMPLOYMENT

There were two methods of payment for shipyard workers depending on the type of work they did – these were piecework and timework.

PIECEWORK

Piecework applied mostly to the platers and riveters etc. of the 'black squad' who made up approximately 40% of all shipyard workers. Platers were organised in squads depending on their particular skill and normally did no other type of plating work. A typical frame squad for example, could comprise four markers each with one helper, four punchers each with two helpers, and two frame setters each with four helpers – a total of ten skilled and twenty unskilled men. A squad leader was appointed who entered into contract with the company for all or portions of frame work in the hull. A price was agreed and for payment purposes the leader's name only was entered into the

company books. Every week the leader was paid money charged against the contract to pay the men in his squad. Payment was sometimes made in the local pub after the leader had collected the money from the piecework office at 12 o'clock on a Saturday.

Riveting squads were paid on the basis of the number of rivets driven. A piecework price list which took into account the difficulty of certain sections of riveting, determined the rate per hundred rivets and this was used to establish a contract price. To determine the total number of rivets driven, a person known as a 'counter' who was a member of the piecework office, was sent to assess the work done. Rivets were counted and marked off with white paint. Caulking was measured by the foot and cancelled in blue paint while work completed by the drillers was counted and painted red. Riveters were paid in similar fashion as platers. Caulkers, drillers and jobbing

A plan of the Naval Construction Works in 1906 showing the awkward location of the Clyde Trusts' workshops and the relatively underdeveloped nature of the shipyard site.

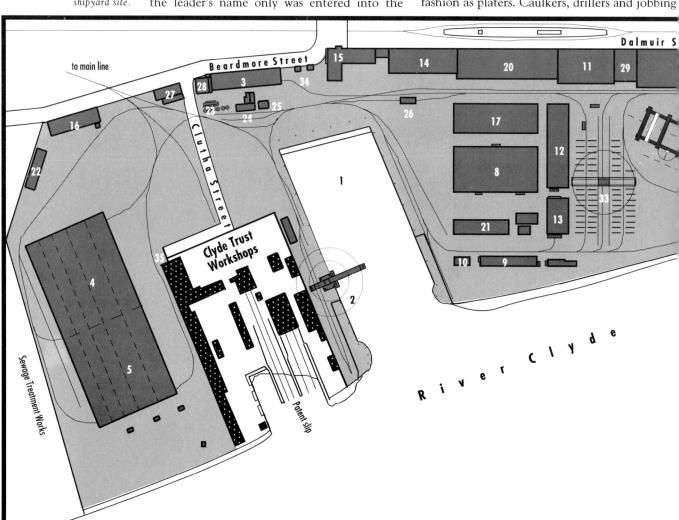

platers, all of whom worked on an individual basis, were paid separately.

TIMEWORK

Most other workers in the yard were time workers who were paid an hourly rate according to the work they did. Some departments operated a bonus scheme. Pattern makers for example, undertaking a job rated at five hours, would be paid for five hours even if the work was completed in four. Wages were paid out on Saturday morning by lining up in order according to works number, outside the time office regardless of weather conditions.

DEMARCATION

The shipyard workforce comprised about 40 different trades together with helpers and labourers. A strict system of demarcation was established primarily to enable employers to hire and discharge trades as required for their specific portion in the construction process. The demarcation system sometimes broke down into 'who does what' disputes but generally favoured the employer in making the most cost effective use of labour.

HOURS OF EMPLOYMENT

Until 1919, the 54 hour week was worked at Dalmuir shipyard. In the morning, work began at 6am and lasted until 9.15am. After breakfast, for which many men went home, work resumed at 10am and continued until 1.15pm. The afternoon began at 2pm and ended at 5.15pm. Saturday working ended at noon. After 1919, the 47 hour week was introduced. This allowed for a starting time of 7.30 in the morning. Any worker arriving even minutes late, found himself locked out and had no alternative but to wait for the gates to open again at breakfast time. The only exception

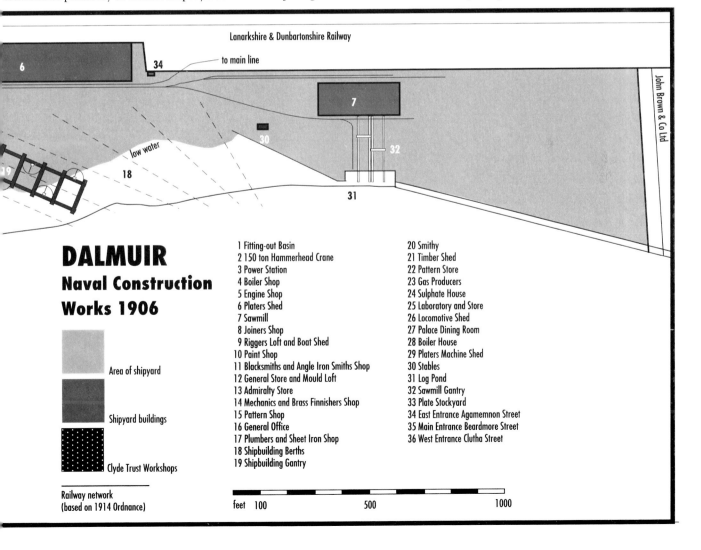

DALMUIR
Naval Construction
Works 1906

Lanarkshire & Dunbartonshire Railway

to main line

low water

John Brown & Co Ltd

Area of shipyard

Shipyard buildings

Clyde Trust Workshops

Railway network
(based on 1914 Ordnance)

1 Fitting-out Basin
2 150 ton Hammerhead Crane
3 Power Station
4 Boiler Shop
5 Engine Shop
6 Platers Shed
7 Sawmill
8 Joiners Shop
9 Riggers Loft and Boat Shed
10 Paint Shop
11 Blacksmiths and Angle Iron Smiths Shop
12 General Store and Mould Loft
13 Admiralty Store
14 Mechanics and Brass Finnishers Shop
15 Pattern Shop
16 General Office
17 Plumbers and Sheet Iron Shop
18 Shipbuilding Berths
19 Shipbuilding Gantry

20 Smithy
21 Timber Shed
22 Pattern Store
23 Gas Producers
24 Sulphate House
25 Laboratory and Store
26 Locomotive Shed
27 Palace Dining Room
28 Boiler House
29 Platers Machine Shed
30 Stables
31 Log Pond
32 Sawmill Gantry
33 Plate Stockyard
34 East Entrance Agamemnon Street
35 Main Entrance Beardmore Street
36 West Entrance Clutha Street

feet 100   500   1000

made to this was if delays were expected on the railway in which case a telephone call was made from Dalmuir station to the shipyard. Holidays did not exist in the sense that they do today; the works simply closed down for ten days in summer for which no payment was made.

MANAGEMENT

The works were managed by a General Manager who had overall control of all departments and activities within the works. His immediate subordinates were the Shipyard Manager and the Engine Works Manager. Thereafter each department had its own manager, head foreman and foremen.

In 1902 senior management, at that time working at Beardmore's Govan yard, attracted the following salaries; General Manager £4,000, Shipyard Manager £2,000 and Engine Works Manager £1,500. By 1921 these salaries had risen to £4,500, £2,500 and £2,200 respectively. In the same year, Lord Invernairn's salary was recorded as £6,000.[31]

Despite running such a large establishment employing up to and over 10,000 persons the General Manager was not entitled to membership of the Board of Directors of the firm.

RIVETED SHIP CONSTRUCTION

In Britain, the practice of riveted ship construction was much the same from one yard to another, the only significant change during the period covered by this book being the continued introduction of pneumatic and hydraulic riveting appliances to elements of construction and the development of enhanced cranage at the berths. The following is a brief description of riveted ship description.

In the ship and engine drawing offices, draughtsmen prepared numerous detailed drawings of the ship and her machinery for use throughout the various departments in the yard. Drawings of the ship's hull known as the body plan, were taken to the mould loft. Here the loftsman scaled-up the body plan and drew this out full scale onto scrieve boards. Scrieve boards were approximately ten feet by six feet in size and had a matt black surface similar to a blackboard. The position of the sheer line, buttock lines, decks and much other information was marked onto each frame on the scrieve boards. The loftsmen also made up certain light wooden templates from the scrieve boards which were supplied to other departments for use in their element of construction. Lying on the floor of the mould loft, the scrieve boards were

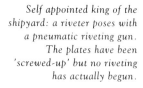

Self appointed king of the shipyard: a riveter poses with a pneumatic riveting gun. The plates have been 'screwed-up' but no riveting has actually begun.

numbered, lifted and reassembled on the floor of the Platers (or Ironworkers) Shed adjacent to the plate and angle furnaces.

The steel trades – platers, angle iron smiths, riveters, caulkers and drillers who actually built the ship, and who were universally known as the 'Black Squad', then took over. Platers were divided into six different squads; shell, frame, beam, bulkhead, deck and jobbers. The frame squad, working at the scrieve boards, made a 'set' for each frame – a bar of soft flat iron formed to the profile of the frame bend required. This set was transferred to the furnace blocks, thick steel beds about five feet square drilled with holes on a grid. To support the set on the blocks, pins were placed behind it at pressure points. The frame to be shaped in the set was heated to red heat or greater in the angle furnace, removed, and manoeuvred by small cranes and winches onto the furnace blocks or, as often, simply dragged from the furnace by helpers using long handled tongs. A hydraulic machine was then used to push the frame into the set. The frame was then left to cool care being taken to ensure that it remained flat. The loftsmans' wooden template, drilled out to indicate the position of rivet holes etc. was laid on the frame and the position of the holes transferred by means of a marking pin. Rivet holes were then punched on the punching machine or drilled if it was a particularly 'heavy' set. The frame was then taken to the rivet bay where a small amount of sub-assembly took place e.g., brackets and beam knees riveted into place. The frame was then taken the short distance to the berth where it was lifted into position by derrick or gantry cranes and bolted to the keel plates already in place on the berth. Shipwrights then 'faired off' each frame, holding the frame in alignment by bolting wooden 'ribands' along the frames. Simultaneously, the beam squad, having imparted the correct camber to each beam in the beam shed, passed them to the shipwrights who laid them across the hull and fixed them to the frames.

The shell squad now made their own wooden templates directly off the ships frames, marking the position of rivet holes etc. in white paint. In the platers shed, this template was in turn used to mark a plate which was then cut to shape on guillotine shears and punched on the punching and shearing machines. If a plate required to be 'set' (curved), this was carried out on the shell or bending rolls. In extreme cases a complex set in more than one direction necessitated the construction of a 'bed' over which a heated plate was bent. Thus the plates were formed and bolted temporarily to the frames strake by strake by squads known as 'screwers up'.

Riveting squads then took over. These could be either machine or hand squads. A hand squad comprised a right and left handed riveter to alternately hammer the rivet, a 'holder on' who was positioned behind the plate to hold the heated rivet in place with a tool called a 'hobey', and a 'heater boy' – who could be 50 or 60 years of age. The heater boy was important as he had to arrange his fire in such a fashion that he had an adequate supply of the different types of rivet likely to be required properly heated and ready for use. The riveter could call out to the heater boy – 'efter four a long yin' or it could be 'a wee yin'. In confined or awkward spaces an additional member of the squad, known as a catch boy, could be employed to insert the rivet. Where a riveting machine was used, the squad comprised a riveter to operate the machine, a holder on and a heater boy. When the riveters had completed their work, caulkers took over. They finished the shell by caulking each plate overlap with a pneumatic caulking machine to ensure an absolutely watertight seam. Simultaneously, other squads would be working on other parts of the ship. In this manner the hull of the ship was constructed to launching stage on the berth. On a large contract such as a battleship or liner, it was not uncommon for between 1,000 and 2,000 men of the black squad to be employed at the same time.

After launching, the hull was towed to the fitting-out basin. Here the ships main and auxiliary machinery together with boilers, all of which would have been built in the various shops while the hull was on the stocks, were lowered into the ship through spaces left in the deck plating. Plating over of these spaces and the construction of the superstructure was then completed while an army of fitting-out trades descended into the ship – electricians, carpenters, engineers, mechanics, riggers, plumbers, painters etc. In the case of a warship, armour plates, turret mechanisms and guns, all of which would have been made outwith the yard, would now be fitted. Outside contractors, relatively few in those days, installed specialist items the yard would not manufacture such as galley equipment, wheelhouse instruments, range finders, searchlights and so on.

Looking over the plate racks in the steel stockyard from the 5 ton Goliath crane. The hull of the Quillota is well advanced on No 1 berth with the gantry behind. Note the use of light pole derricks on No 1 berth.

A HESITANT START: 1904 – 1909

Throughout the construction of the new yard at Dalmuir, shipbuilding and marine engineering continued at the Company's Govan and Lancefield establishments. Admiralty contracts had previously formed a significant part of the work undertaken at the old yard and indeed, under Robert Napier's direction, the *Black Prince*, sister ship of the *Warrior*, the world's first ocean going ironclad, was built at Govan between the years 1859 and 1862. The wrought iron armour for this ship was produced by Beardmore at Parkhead in 1861. Since acquiring the Govan yard in 1900, Beardmore had been anxious to maintain and improve upon this long association with the Royal Navy and orders for two first class armoured cruisers had been secured. The first of these, the *Berwick*, was completed in 1903 the second, the *Carnarvon*, in 1905. The latter vessel completed fitting-out in the new basin at Dalmuir. Several merchant vessels, a steam yacht and a naval tug were also built at Govan during this period, the very last vessel to be launched being the small steamer *Highland Laddie* on 20 April 1905. The engines for these vessels were constructed at the Lancefield works.

By the spring of 1905, work on the new yard was sufficiently advanced, especially the completion of the shipbuilding gantry, to permit the first orders to proceed. The final transfer of men and machinery from the old establishments to the new was effected by 12 am on 28 May 1905 whereupon the old works were put up for sale.[1] The first vessel to be laid down in the new yard was the 450 ton steam yacht *Zaza* built for William Beardmore himself and launched by his wife on 5

The Monmouth Class armoured cruiser Berwick built at the Govan yard and completed in December 1903

The armoured cruiser Carnarvon of the Devonshire Class was built at Govan but completed fitting-out at Dalmuir.

The steam yacht Zaza the first vessel launched at Dalmuir shipyard. Built for William Beardmore, the Zaza was subsequently used as an armed patrol vessel during the First World War.

The Lord Nelson Class battleship Agamemnon under the gantry shortly before her launch.

been 'invited' to tender for one of the two battleships of the Lord Nelson class to be built under the 1904/1905 Estimates. In total, eight yards tendered for the two contracts and of these Beardmore and Palmers were successful.[2]

The Beardmore contract was for the hull, exclusive of the main propelling machinery, the contract for which was awarded to Hawthorn Leslie on Tyneside. It was not uncommon, even when shipyards had their own engine works, for contracts to be split in this way. In this instance however, the engine works at Dalmuir were incomplete and not in a position to carry out the work.

The keel of the *Agamemnon* was laid down under the new gantry on 15 May 1905 and brought to the launching stage, with all 15 Yarrow water tube boilers in place, by 23 June the following year.[3] This was two months quicker than her sister ship, *Lord Nelson*, also built under a gantry, although of a different type, at Palmers Yard. The month of June 1906 did much to highlight the pre-eminence of the shipbuilding industry in Britain, and of Clydeside in particular, for within the space of three weeks, two ships representing the largest examples of their type were launched within a mile of each other. The *Lusitania*, the

July 1905. The building of such a small vessel as the *Zaza* was helpful in that it assisted in the creation of working practices at the new yard and also permitted the Company to retain a nucleus of key workers from the Govan yard for apart from one other order, there were no orders for the new yard at all. Fortunately the other order, for the battleship *Agamemnon*, was highly significant, symbolising an almost immediate justification for William Beardmore's extensive new works. A year earlier, on 8 August 1904, Beardmore had

largest and fastest liner so far built, took to the water at John Brown's yard on the 7th, followed by the *Agamemnon*, the most powerful warship in the world, on the 23rd. (This double launching was repeated later in the same year when the *Lord Nelson* and the *Mauretania* were launched on Tyneside in September). Largely because of these vessels, the month of June 1906 created a record on Clydeside with launchings totalling 124,544 tons. The year 1906 set a new shipbuilding record in the UK with 1,828,000 tons of mercantile shipping launched despite a strike by boilermakers on the Clyde which lasted for seven weeks affecting 20,000 men.[4]

In a district where launchings were commonplace, such vessels nevertheless created considerable interest. For the launching of the *Agamemnon*, two special trains were run from Glasgow Central conveying an estimated two thousand people to join the thousands of locals already in the yard as well as those on the opposite side of the river. As the crowds gathered around the carefully cordoned-off hull, the local brass band struck up a series of rousing melodies. The launching platform was draped in crimson and gold fabric upon which the name *Agamemnon* was emblazoned in gilt letters on a blue field. The

launch was timed for 1pm but the movement of two Allan liners on the river caused a delay of a few moments. On the platform, the Countess of Aberdeen in company with William Beardmore and numerous other dignitaries, performed the launching ceremony to the strain of Rule Britannia as finally, the battleship *Agamemnon* slid from underneath the gantry into the dark waters of the River Clyde.[5] Her launching weight was 7,000 tons. This event marked the official opening of the Naval Construction Works.

The fitting-out of the *Agamemnon* was subject to several delays and another two years elapsed before she was completed. This was largely the result of the building, in secrecy, of the revolutionary battleship *Dreadnought* at Portsmouth Dockyard. Quite apart from her technical significance, the *Dreadnought* had unique importance for the armaments companies in the United Kingdom. On completion in December 1906, this battleship with a uniform main armament of ten heavy guns as opposed to a mixed calibre main armament which had been standard until then, and steam turbines for her motive power instead of reciprocating machinery, created nothing less than a sensation. At a stroke, her arrival had rendered all existing battleships

Launch of the Agamemnon on 23 June 1906 marking the official opening of the Naval Construction Works.

The big Russian armoured cruiser Rurik alongside the Agamemnon in 1908. The Rurik was built by Vickers at Barrow but completed fitting-out at Dalmuir. The Rurik appears to be larger than the Agamemnon despite the latters' battleship status. Rurik was 85 feet longer although displaced almost 1,000 tons less. The area to the right of the crane shows workshops which were formerly part of the Clyde Trust Workshops. This area was to be cleared in preparation for building a very large dry dock.

obsolete and immediately eliminated or at best, relegated to the second rank, the vast preponderance of British pre-dreadnought battleships upon which the Two Power Standard was founded. The sudden appearance of the *Dreadnought* had all but levelled the British numerical advantage in capital ships and, in the assumption that other nations would grasp at the opportunity to build their own Dreadnoughts, virtually demanded a period of sustained building to re-establish the dominance of the seas which British policy required. Although unquestionably a technical first for the Royal Navy and a step in which there was little choice for fear of a rival nation building such a ship, the Dreadnought had the direct effect of intensifying Anglo-German naval rivalry and made the construction of a German fleet only slightly numerically inferior if not equal to the British, a distinct possibility. German response, enshrined in Admiral Von

Tirpitz's Naval Laws, became ever more set on the creation of a fleet with which war 'even for her most powerful opponent would be a dangerous affair'.

In the summer of 1907, four Dreadnought type battleships of the Nassau class were laid down in German yards signalling a challenge which the British could not afford to ignore. This development, hardly foreseeable in 1900, could only have been viewed with a degree of commercial satisfaction by the armaments companies who had invested heavily in plant and facilities for battleship production.

While the implications following the appearance of the *Dreadnought* were felt at home and abroad, the *Agamemnon* lying incomplete on the Clyde, was affected in a much more direct sense. First Sea Lord Sir John Fisher's desire to present the *Dreadnought* to the world as a *fait accompli*, demanded an exceptionally rapid

building time of only one year (14 months in reality) To sustain this rate of construction, the main armament turrets and mountings intended for the *Agamemnon* and the *Lord Nelson* which had already been manufactured, were diverted to the *Dreadnought* as the manufacture of these extremely complex mechanisms was often the most time consuming element in warship construction. *Agamemnon's* completion was subject to additional delays which were attributed to continual alteration made to her design during building and insufficient notice given to sub-contractors for the manufacture of equipment.[6]

While the *Agamemnon* languished at her fitting-out berth, events for the Naval Construction Works were not entirely encouraging. No new naval orders had been secured and the first ship orders to be received since the *Agamemnon* – four steamers for the Pacific Steam Navigation Company – had not been booked until March 1906. These vessels, the *Quillota, Quilpué, Huanchaco* and *Junin* intended for passenger and mail service on the west coast of

South America, were nevertheless built rapidly. The *Quilpué* of 3,669 tons gross, was handed over in 319 working days from placing the order while the *Quillota* was even shorter at 246 working days. Employment returns for the shipyard are unknown for this period but it seems likely, from press reports of the time, that around 4,000 persons were employed at the height of the *Agamemnon's* construction.[7] With the launching of the latter and the four cargo ships, a large number of steel workers were out of work. In the absence of a continuous supply of work, it was normal practice to lay off trades once their element in the process of construction was complete, although some effort was made to retain foremen and apprentices. 1906 had nevertheless been a record year of output in the UK with total tonnage exceeding two million for the first time. However, the harsh realities of the shipbuilding industry are well illustrated by the output figure for 1908 which plunged to almost half that of 1906 with dire consequences for shipyard workers. Merchant shipbuilding during the years 1907 to 1910 was

The Pacific Steam Navigation Company's Quilpué leaving Dalmuir to run trials in May 1907.

depressed generally and even naval orders were at first kept in check by the Government of the day anxious not to fan the flames of the naval race developing between Britain and Germany.

The vessels on order at Dalmuir did not represent a large order book for such a large establishment and inevitably, as these orders were progressed through the yard, further layoffs occurred. This happened in May 1907 when a large number of carpenters were dismissed following the departure of the *Quilpué* upriver to Govan dry docks for a hull examination prior to trials and her maiden voyage to Valparaiso.[8] More layoffs were narrowly averted, when in May 1907, another order for the Pacific Steam Navigation Company was won. This was for the 11,500 gross ton twin screw passenger cargo ship *Orcoma*. This

ship, also for the South American trade, carried 1,150 passengers of whom 250 were first class, 200 second class, 100 third class and 600 steerage. Accommodation for first class passengers was magnificent – the dining saloon was decorated in the Adams style with woodwork of a pale golden colour rendered in French ormolu gold.[9]

On 19 August, the Beardmore works again attracted the interest of senior Admiralty personnel when Admiral Lord Charles Beresford, Vice Admiral Sir Reginald Custance and fifty officers of the Channel Fleet which was lying at Lamlash visited the Parkhead and Dalmuir works. Steam trials for the *Agamemnon* commenced on the same day ending satisfactorily on the 26th.[10] When the *Agamemnon* was dry docked at Govan she injured her rudder which necessitated a new

Two cylindrical Scotch boilers on the transporter about to be hauled by the works' locomotives to the fitting-out basin to be installed on the Quillota in December 1906. Each of these boilers weighed 60 tons. The man to the left with the long white beard is Mr W W May, the Engine Works manager.

one being manufactured at Parkhead. The order for the 20 ton cast steel rudder frame was placed with the foundry on 23 December 1907, and the complete rudder despatched to the dock on 25 January 1907.[11]

Towards the end of 1907, an event occurred which gave insight into the relationship existing between the Beardmore and Vickers companies. In late 1907, proposals for a new type of submarine boat were in preparation by Beardmore when Lieutenant Trevor Dawson, a director of both Vickers and Beardmore, interceded to block the effort on the basis that the capital outlay could not be justified by Beardmore in light of that Company's poor financial position. Dawson added that Beardmore's present situation had been brought about by over capital expenditure on

plant – referring to Dalmuir – when no demand existed and urged Beardmore to pursue remunerative work along the lines for which the Dalmuir yard had been laid out. In reply to Dawson, The Marquis of Graham, a strong ally of William Beardmore, vigorously defended the Beardmore Company's right to pursue any form of naval construction. Vickers concern over William Beardmores' desire to extend what they clearly considered to be an unjustifiably large and expensive establishment at Dalmuir, is understandable although, it should be added, that Vickers had entered into secret agreement with the Admiralty whereby Vickers were guaranteed all orders for submarines to be built in private yards.[12] Details of the Beardmore 1907 submarine proposals are not known. In this instance, Vickers

The 11,533 ton Orcoma in the fitting-out basin in August 1908. The Orcoma was the largest of four ships built for the Pacific Steam Navigation Company. She served as an armed merchant cruiser during the First World War.

A view of Dalmuir shipyard taken in 1907 from the top of the John Brown 150 ton cantilever crane. The excellent position of the berths, with an uninterrupted launching run upstream is clear. John Brown's west yard berths and sawmill are in the foreground the latter marking the boundary with Dalmuir shipyard. This panorama also shows the newly built tenements on Dunbarton Road and their relationship to the yard.

were successful in restraining Beardmore, however, a submarine yard was built at Dalmuir in 1913.

In December 1908, the Company introduced a period of short time working in view of the poor order book, the day starting at 8 am and finishing at 4 pm with a one hour lunch break and no Saturday working.[13] In January of the following year, the Vickers Company, viewing the deteriorating situation at Dalmuir and their interest in the Beardmore Company with some concern, sent the powerful armoured cruiser *Rurik*, recently built at Barrow for the Russian Government, to Dalmuir for final adjustments during her trials period. This was not the first Barrow built warship to visit Dalmuir. On 1 May 1906 Vickers sent the Japanese battleship *Katori*

to Dalmuir for machinery inspection after running trials on the Firth of Clyde.[14] The difficult position of the shipyard was made strikingly obvious when the *Orcoma* was launched in April 1908 – the building berths were empty and only the *Agamemnon* and the *Rurik* remained in the basin in the final stages of fitting-out. On 22 March the *Agamemnon* left Dalmuir to run further trials in the Firth of Clyde whereupon 500 men were paid off. During the trials period, which lasted many months, a similar number of men travelled daily to the battleship's moorings off Craigendoran pier to administer the final touches to the ship. When the ship was handed over in September, they too were paid-off.[15] Not surprisingly, a pessimistic note was sounded in the local newspaper – *The*

Clydebank Press on 28 July 1908 –

'. . . the condition of Messrs Beardmore's yard at Dalmuir is giving cause for great anxiety . . . '

The Director's report for 1907, disclosed a loss of £122,672 3s 3d. In accounting for this, the report blamed 'the continuance of the unfavourable state of trade and labour difficulties.' As a consequence the Company had no alternative but to cut costs to the minimum including the dismissal of many foremen. When the *Orcoma* was completed in August, there was a further reduction in staff amidst the rumour that the yard would close altogether.

1908 was a particularly severe year for shipbuilding; shipping freights slumped resulting in reduced demand for new tonnage, while warship construction on the Clyde alone had slipped from approximately 50,000 tons to 5,000 tons in the space of only two years. Unemployment among trade union members across the industry was 25.2% compared with 9.3% in 1907.[16] Many shipyards made serious financial losses prompting an almost universal reduction in wages of from 5 to 10%. Between a third to a half of all skilled workers had been idle for most of the year.[17]

Unsuccessful attempts were made during 1908 by Beardmore to become involved in the consortium formed to re-equip the Spanish fleet. The Company was also unsuccessful in September when tenders for three 27 knot torpedo boats for the Admiralty at £115,100 for the first, £112,100 for the second and £116,600 for the third, were

not accepted.[18] In the same month, the *Rurik* left to run trials leaving the yard with no shipbuilding work whatsoever.

In the Engine and Boiler shops however, employment was secured by an order book which included seven sets of gas engines of the Oechelhauser type and ancillary equipment for the Associated Portland Cement Company. A series of boilers for Roumanian State Railways was under construction for installation in the steamship *Constanza* as were the boilers for a small cruiser, the *Almirante Grau*, being built for the Peruvian Navy by Vickers at Barrow.

During this period, the Company first expressed interest in new and novel forms of marine propulsion. This interest, which remained with the Company throughout and was later extended to aircraft and locomotives, was often carried to great lengths in the design, manufacture and testing of engines. Experimental gas and semi-diesel engines were developed in the engine works for a lengthy period before the First World War and in the case of gas engines, the works were responsible for most of the pioneering work undertaken in this country. Gas engines were

The battleship Agamemnon *during her trials period on the Firth of Clyde in 1908. The building of* Agamemnon *was subject to delay partly because of Sir John Fisher's desire to complete the revolutionary battleship* Dreadnought *at great speed. This resulted in the main armament intended for* Agamemnon *being diverted to Portsmouth where* Dreadnought *was building.*

widely employed on land for a variety of purposes, including the Beardmore works among many, and it seemed perfectly possible that suitably modified, these engines could be made to propel a ship. The Beardmore Company accumulated considerable experience in the design and manufacture of gas engines for land use and as early as 1903, had acquired the British rights to the manufacture of the Capitaine gas engine in conjunction with J I Thornycroft, the Thames torpedo-boat builders. The gas engines developed by Herr Capitaine of Frankfurt, were of limited power and suitable for small craft only but nevertheless provided a starting point for further development work. In 1905 two small experimental Capitaine gas engines were constructed at Dalmuir 'to be tried out on William Robertson's boats' and one of them, complete with producer plant, was fitted in the small launch appropriately named *Dalmuir*. Design studies based on this engine undertaken by W W May, the Engine Works manager, showed that in a 7,000 ton cargo vessel with reciprocating machinery developing 2,000 ihp, a weight saving of 25% and a space saving of 13,000 cubic feet, would be achieved by installing gas engines of the same

power. This promised significant benefits in the economic operation of ships and encouraged the Company to further develop this engine.[19]

As the launch *Dalmuir* proved successful, a much larger five cylinder engine of 555 bhp was built and put under test. At first bituminous coal was burnt in the producer and found to be less than satisfactory. With modification to the producer, anthracite was successfully substituted. The problem of what vessel to install the experimental engine in was solved by the Marquis of Graham who, as the Commander of the Clyde Royal Naval Volunteer Reserve at Govan, suggested the old 750 ton gun boat *Rattler*, training ship of the Reserve. With Admiralty consent, Rattler was made available as a trials ship.[20] In 1907 the old steam plant was removed and the new gas engine installed. In this form, a series of trials were undertaken in the *Rattler* and in the space of one year, the vessel travelled a distance of 7,500 miles without serious mishap. It seems likely that several attempts at making a successful engine were tried as the sum of £168 is recorded in the accounts for 1909 as representing 'the scrap value of the Capitaine engines taken out of *Rattler*'. As a gas engined ship, the engine room complement of the *Rattler* dropped from 17 to 7 hands. Difficulty was encountered with the hydraulic clutch necessary for reversing the engine and, according to the Marquis of Graham, ' . . . gave us more trouble through constant slipping than all the rest of the engine put together'.[21] In June 1910, the *Rattler* left Dalmuir for Portsmouth Dockyard where she was evaluated by naval engineering personnel. After trials, it was found that machinery of this type was indeed better suited to smaller craft and the idea, although initially promising, was dropped.

Alongside experimental work on gas engines, the Company also pursued the development of small two-stroke semi-diesels based on the 'Peck' type. By means of demonstrating the suitability of this engine, the Marquis of Graham assisted once more by fitting a 130 bhp Beardmore semi-diesel in his yacht *Mairi*, which was building up-river at the yard of Ritchie Graham and Milne during 1910. Continuous development of this engine took place over the next few years and a catalogue of Beardmore two-stroke semi-diesel engines produced in 1913, listed eight engines ranging in

The twin quadruple expansion engines of the Orcoma. *These engines developed 12,000 ihp and were capable of driving the ship at a creditable 17 knots.*

power from 30 to 260 bhp. These engines were shipped to destinations as far away as New Zealand and Shanghai for installation into locally built vessels although many were fitted to fishing boats, pilot craft and other small vessels at Dalmuir.

In November 1908, a year of speculation and uncertainty over the future of the Naval Construction Works ended when the order for the second class cruiser *Gloucester*, of the Bristol Class, was announced. The placing of this order marked the end of an exceptionally difficult period as well as the beginning of increased demand for warships of all classes, a demand which did not cease until 1918.

Early in 1909, two very small contracts were won, the first of which was the lighthouse tender *Pharos* for the Northern Lighthouse Commission, the other being for the sludge boat *Shieldhall* for Glasgow Corporation Sewage Department. Ten shipyards tendered for the latter order on which Beardmore made an £83 loss – the *Pharos* broke even – and it seems likely that the objective was more to do with keeping personnel together than tendering at realistic prices.

Following the launch of the *Gloucester* by the Marchioness of Graham in October 1909, William Beardmore was able to announce that a second cruiser order had been won. This was for the *Falmouth*, a slightly improved version of the *Gloucester* with an enhanced main armament. Better news followed on the 30th of December when the Company was informed by the Admiralty that their tender for HMS *Conqueror*, one of four 'contingency' battleships of the Orion class had been provisionally accepted. Of the nine private firms that submitted tenders, three were successful – Beardmore, Armstrong and Thames Iron Works. The fourth ship went to Portsmouth Dockyard.

Since the *Agamemnon* had been ordered in 1904, the Company had failed, for a period of four years, to win any Admiralty work whatsoever, and even when they did succeed, it was only for the small cruiser *Gloucester* in November 1908. This was the poorest performance of any of the warship yards over the same period when Armstrong, Fairfield and John Brown had each laid down two Dreadnoughts and Vickers, Scotts and Palmers had one. Although naval orders were pursued vigorously, the lack of results had been depressing. When the Admiralty asked the Company to submit tenders in the autumn of 1906 for Bellerophon Class battleships, it was for the hull only and not for the machinery. This prompted the Marquis of Graham to write to the First Lord of the Admiralty Lord Tweeddale —

'I would like to say to you privately that we have sunk an enormous amount of capital in establishing the great naval construction works at Dalmuir, and it is a serious thing to be denied any chance of getting Government work to do in any particular line . . . All I respectfully ask is that you may see your way clear to give Wm Beardmore and Coy. permission to tender for engines and machinery as well as for hull and armour of the new battleships, and so in some degree grant us encouragement in return for the efforts we have made to establish naval construction works which may be of as great credit as of use to the nation.'[22]

Despite Admiralty agreement to this request, no order for either hull or machinery was placed for battleships of the Bellerophon or succeeding classes until the *Conqueror* of the Orion class in December 1909. From the cruiser Gloucester onwards, Beardmore constructed the machinery and boilers for all the warships built in the yard. Plant for the manufacture of turbines was installed in the engine shops during 1909.[23]

Merchant orders had by no means compensated for the lack of naval work and setting aside the generally depressed state of the shipbuilding industry, the lack of an established relationship with a shipping line, such as enjoyed by many yards, was partly to blame. Apart from re-introducing naval work to the yard, the *Gloucester* was also significant in that she was the first ship built at Dalmuir that actually made a profit for the Company. A profit of £30,142 was made out of a total contract price plus extras of £301,537.

Although an improvement in the order book had taken place, it did not stop the Company complaining vigorously over Clydebank Councils assessed valuation of the yard which had been fixed at £15,000. This compared with £13,500 for John Brown and £22,000 for the Singer factory although these figures reflected the area of the works not the level of activity within. The Company claimed that £10,000 was the true figure while the newspaper that reported this case added that it was well known that the yard had not lived up to expectations.[24]

The order for the *Conqueror* underlined the vagaries of naval procurement during this period, for had it not been for the pressure of public opinion on the Government brought about as a result of the naval scare of 1909, the *Conqueror* and her three sister ships might not have been built at all. Initially it had been intended to lay down a total of four new Dreadnoughts under the 1909 Programme instead of the eight eventually ordered. However, public alarm at the number of Dreadnoughts reported to be building in German yards, coupled with fears of a dramatic expansion of the Krupp ordnance works and German shipyard capacity, raised the issue of the 1909 Programme to one of supreme national importance. Largely due to the efforts of the First Lord of the Admiralty, Reginald McKenna, and a press campaign characterised by the slogan 'we want eight and we won't wait', the Government reluctantly gave way and eventually, four additional battleships were ordered including the four Orions which earned them the title 'contingency' ships. Between July 1909 and June 1910 the keels of no fewer then 10 Dreadnoughts had been laid down – four of them on the Clyde.

Fears over German ability to outbuild British yards were groundless as events were to prove. British shipbuilding capacity far exceeded anything the Germans could hope to match and building times were in any case longer in German yards although this perhaps reflected a different attitude to construction rather than lack of speed. At the height of the 1909 battleship controversy, the Marquis of Graham, never slow to put the Beardmore name forward, made the following statement to the press which was printed on 20 March 1909:

'As a director of Wm Beardmore and Co., I may say that we can lay down two dreadnoughts at once and in the course of four months we could lay out a third slip for another dreadnought. We have the plant and the means also of turning out the armour, and guns of all calibres, and each ship could be ready within two years of laying down the keel.'[25]

Four days later the Times Engineering Supplement went a little further declaring that 'Messrs Vickers, Armstrong and Beardmore can each lay down and carry forward four Dreadnoughts . . . at the same time'. Elsewhere on the Clyde, according to local newspaper reports, Fairfield and Brown each had two slips available where battleships could be laid down and Scotts had one.[26]

While berths may indeed have been available as described above, the building of battleships on this scale would have made simultaneous construction impossible on labour grounds alone, even without considering armour and main armament supply. However, sentiments such as these expressed in difficult times, even although incapable of realisation, were no doubt reassuring.

In the space of one year the fortunes of the Naval Construction Works had been transformed largely as a result of the increasing pace of the naval race. The order book now stood at one battleship, two cruisers, a lighthouse tender and a sludge boat. While this was a great improvement, it was still not representative of the yard's capacity.

The Agamemnon *as completed in 1908.*

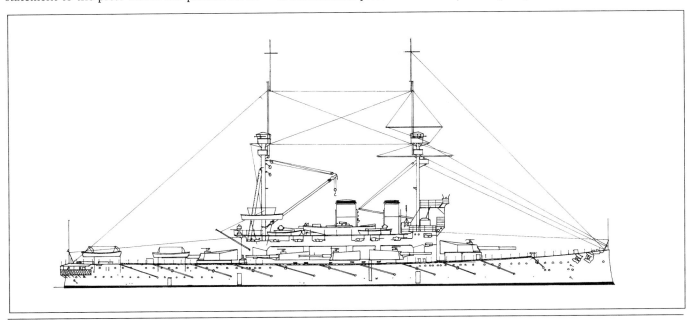

STEADY PROGRESS: 1910 – 1913

In May 1910, the First Lord, Reginald McKenna in company with the Third Sea Lord (Controller) Sir John Jellicoe, made a routine tour of inspection of naval work in progress on Clydeside.[1] At Dalmuir they saw both the *Conqueror* and *Falmouth* in frame while the *Gloucester* was in the basin being made ready for sea trials. The latter ship had been launched in October 1909 after only 150 days on the building slip. Later that year the *Pharos* and *Shieldhall* were completed and the *Falmouth*, a little longer on the slips than her sister at seven months, was launched in September. The launch of a ship was usually followed by a luncheon for invited guests which was held in the mould loft. It was also the occasion on which William Beardmore or other speakers would comment on the ship or on the state of trade in general. After the *Falmouth* was launched, Sir John Jellicoe in proposing the builder said;

> 'The firm of Wm Beardmore and Co., was distinguished for many characteristics among others for its enterprise. Those who visited the Clyde could not fail to be struck, even in passing up the river, by the magnificence of the plant, which was visible for miles in every direction, but it required a closer inspection of the yard to fully appreciate the enterprise which had brought together such a wonderful accumulation of plant'[2]

In the following year the Company won its first destroyer order for the *Goshawk* of the Acheron class and soon after yet another cruiser, *Dublin*, was added to the total of ships on order. This gave the yard more naval work than any of the other yards on the Clyde for the first time. The total value of naval work at Dalmuir was estimated at £2¾ million.[3] In March 1911, there was a revival of merchant work at Dalmuir when the Adelaide Steamship Company Limited announced the placing of a three ship order with the yard for the 7,700 ton passenger cargo vessels *Willochra*, *Wandilla* and *Warilda*. Once again however, these contracts were taken on at commercially unrealistic prices and a huge loss of £173,586 was made on the three vessels.

The *Conqueror* was launched on 1 May 1911 and as with the *Agamemnon* five years previously, the launching of the Navy's newest battleship attracted considerable interest. The launching party included the Secretary of State for Scotland, Lord Pentland and his wife, Admiral Bearcroft, Admiral Adair and Colonel Armstrong,– the

Vickers representative on the Beardmore board. The best view of the impending launch however, probably went to the passengers of the Clyde paddle steamer *Glen Lyon* which had been stopped, by the port authorities in attendance, in mid channel to clear the area. A few minutes after 2 pm, the Clydebank Brass Band struck up the obligatory Rule Britannia and the *Conqueror*, dressed from stem to stern in bunting, was launched into the Clyde by Lady Pentland. She took 58 seconds to come to a rest whereupon she was taken-up by the waiting tugs and towed to her berth in the fitting-out basin. Her launching weight was almost 11,000 tons and all 18 of her boilers and some armour were already in place.[4]

At the luncheon held after the launch, William Beardmore referred to the lock-out of the previous year which had delayed the battleship for almost four months. This dispute arose because the Shipbuilding Employers Federation felt that the Boilermakers, 'notorious for going their own way' were in breach of agreement every time a local dispute ended in a walk out 'without due and proper notice being given'. On 9 March 1909, the National Shipyard Agreement had been signed between the Employers and the main 18 shipyard unions concerned in an attempt to deal with any matters affecting the industry at the same time.[5]

This agreement was unable to prevent the 1910 lock-out however and both sides initially took-up strong positions. The lock-out came into effect on 3 September and approximately 20,000 boilermakers, mainly on the Clyde and North East Coast, were affected. This action resulted in an estimated 20,000 men of other trades being laid-off. The lock-out ended on 15 December with both sides having shifted their positions considerably allowing for the signing of a supplementary agreement and the setting-up of new machinery to hear grievances.[6]

As a result of this dispute, the *Conqueror*'s one year and 26 days on the stocks gave her the longest period on the stocks of any Dreadnought battleship to have been built in a British yard. The original contract completion date was 1 April 1912 which allowed for what had come to be generally accepted as the normal building time of two years for a British battleship. The *Conqueror* ran the first of her contractor's trials on 21 May followed by her 30 hours trial on 5 June. Full power trials on 7 June were highly satisfactory, the ship proving to be the fastest of her class on trials with a recorded

speed of 22.126 knots at 33,198 shp. She was finally accepted into service in November of that year.

The *Conqueror* had been constructed almost entirely from Beardmore made parts, the major exception being the manufacture of the hydraulic mountings for the 13.5 inch main armament. This remained the one activity in which the Company, unlike Vickers, the Coventry Syndicate and Armstrong, had no capacity. The main and secondary armament gun barrels as well as all the heavy armour were manufactured at the parent works at Parkhead as was a fair proportion of armour and armament for battleships building elsewhere.

A small gun mounting department was established at Dalmuir in 1910 primarily to make the four and six inch gun mountings for the secondary armament to be fitted in the *Conqueror* and subsequent battleships built at the yard.[7] While this development had been part of William Beardmore's original plan to build the largest shipyard and gun factory outside the Royal Dockyards, as built in 1910, this modest facility was not capable of making the very large main armament mountings. In 1908, the Company had approached the Admiralty with new designs for a four inch mounting which had been accepted.[8] This resulted in Beardmore being placed on the very short list of gun mounting manufacturers for weapons of that calibre. Strictly speaking, in the

case of main armament mountings, this dependency on other firms for such an essential part of ordnance hardware, robbed Beardmore of the claim to complete capability over every aspect of manufacture within his works.

Conqueror's main armament mountings were manufactured relatively close to hand by the Coventry Ordnance Works who, in 1905, had set up large shops at Coventry and Scotstoun on the Clyde for this purpose. At Scotstoun, the heavy guns, turrets and mountings intended for the *Conqueror* or battleships building elsewhere on the Clyde, were assembled and tested prior to being shipped by barge down river to Dalmuir for installation under the hammerhead crane.

Meanwhile, the cruiser *Falmouth* had been brought to her steam trials three months ahead of contract and in June 1911, completed successful speed, gun, torpedo and manoeuvring trials on the Firth of Clyde. All that remained to be done before handing over was a final machinery inspection. In September, the Allan Line ordered two passenger liners for the North Atlantic from Clyde yards. Of the twelve yards which had tendered, Beardmore won the Al*satian*, later known as the *Empress of France*, which at 18,450 tons was slightly larger than her sister ship, the *Calgarian*, which went to Fairfield.

1911 marked the start of what was to be a series of record years for shipbuilding in the United Kingdom, culminating in the all time high of 1913 when 2,311,960 tons of shipping was launched. Naval work contributed greatly to output and on the Clyde alone, during 1911, it was estimated that over 20,000 men were employed solely on naval work.[9]

At Dalmuir, continuity of work for years ahead was assured when the Company learned that it had been successful in tendering for yet another battleship. This was for the *Benbow* of the Iron Duke class which had been authorised under the 1911 Estimates. Throughout 1912, work proceeded on an order book which more accurately, and for the first time, reflected the shipyard's capacity. In the spring of that year this stood at three passenger cargo vessels (7,555 tons each), a passenger liner (18,500 tons), two battleships (55,000 tons together), a cruiser (6,000 tons) and a destroyer (900 tons), a figure of over 100,000 tons whether one counts in gross tons for merchant vessels or displacement tons for warships. The Engine Works supplied the main propelling machinery for all

The three drum water tube boilers of the cruiser Royalist *fully assembled in the boiler shop awaiting transportation to the fitting-out basin on 9 July 1914.*

these vessels which ranged from single screw quadruple expansion machinery for the cargo vessels to quadruple screw direct drive steam turbines for the liner and warships.

As originally equipped, the Engine Works were capable of building traditional reciprocating machinery only as steam turbines, although in use, were confined to a few experimental installations to assess their potential. When it became clear that turbines would replace reciprocating machinery in many types of ships – and particularly after their choice for the battleship *Dreadnought* – the Company acquired manufacturing rights from the Parsons company in January 1905 and later installed the plant necessary for their manufacture. Initial Admiralty reluctance to seek tenders from Beardmore for machinery of this type, may well have reflected uncertainty over ability to construct the new technology turbine engines.

Despite the size of the engine works at Dalmuir, the Company was unable to attract the volume of orders for the plant on anything like the scale of the other two battleship builders on the upper reaches of the river, John Brown and Fairfield, both of whom regularly constructed turbine sets for battleships and battlecruisers building in the Royal Dockyards. Beardmore's only prewar success in this area was in 1911 when the order to build the machinery for the cruiser *Fearless* building at Chatham Dockyard was won.

During the years 1912/13, several significant staff appointments were made. The first, in September 1912, was the appointment of Archibald Jack Campbell as General Manager at a salary of £4,500, following the retiral of Edmund Sharer. Campbell, like Sharer, was a man of considerable shipbuilding experience who came

The first of three photographs showing the Conqueror *fitting-out.*
August 1911: The battleship is in the early stages of fitting-out while the Town Class cruiser Falmouth *is raising steam ready for trials.*

AJ Campbell, General Manager of the Naval Construction Works from 1913 until 1927.

April 1912: Conqueror nears completion. The cruiser Dublin and the destroyer Goshawk are alongside giving a good indication of the relative sizes of these classes of warship.

to be widely respected in Dalmuir both professionally and in his association with the local community. A native of Clydebank, Campbell served an apprenticeship in the drawing office at J & G Thomson's shipyard in the 1880s. He then worked in Spain for Palmers Shipbuilding Company in connection with warships which were being built for the Spanish Navy at Bilbao. Between the years 1901 and 1909, he was shipyard manager at Vickers in Barrow and it was during this period that Vickers, in association with Armstrong, were successful in their joint bid to provide technical assistance in the rebuilding of the Spanish Navy. Campbell, already fluent in Spanish, was appointed Chief Director of Works over the British consortium. Under his control, a series of warships were constructed including three small battleships at Ferrol Dockyard and gun boats and destroyers at Cartagena. Campbell took a great interest in the welfare of youths in the

Dalmuir area and was active in the local Boys' Brigade Company. He was also a prominent member of the Dalmuir 'Wee Free' church.

In July 1913, Captain William Onyon was appointed Assistant Chief Engineer of the Engine Works with a salary of £1,500 plus £50 per annum for life insurance. Onyon was newly retired from the Royal Navy where he had been Chief Engineer on the *Dreadnought*. On coming ashore, he had been made responsible for overseeing construction of all turbine machinery for the Navy's battleships. Suitably experienced service personnel were often sought by the armaments companies as much for their influence and understanding of the Service as for technical knowledge.

In similar vein, links with a major shipping line were maintained if not positively cultivated when, in February 1913, Colonel J Smith Park was appointed to the Beardmore board on the retiral of Colonel D C Armstrong. Smith Park had

been Managing Director of the Glasgow based Allan Line until his retiral from that position in August of the previous year. Although Beardmore was already building for the Allan Line, the prospect of further orders which this appointment might have encouraged, were dashed by the onset of the First World War.

In the last few years leading up to the War, the accelerating demand for warships obliged the private warship yards to devote less time to merchant work. At Dalmuir, 1913 was marked by the laying down of a cross section of warship types which had been ordered under the 1912/13 programme. These were the destroyers *Lennox* and *Llewellyn* of the Laforey class and the light scout cruisers *Galatea*, *Inconstant* and *Royalist* of the Arethusa class. In August the Company's tender for a Revenge class battleship was provisionally accepted – final confirmation was received on 18 September. Thus the battleship *Ramillies* was the fourth to be ordered in nine years from a yard specifically brought into existence for their construction. Despite the general inability of Dalmuir shipyard to attract orders on a scale commensurate with its capacity, the four battleship orders nevertheless compare favourably with most of the other private naval yards with the exception of Armstrong and Vickers, both of whom pursued vigorously successful sales policies abroad. In the ten year period preceding the start of the War, the distribution of battleship and battlecruiser orders up to and including the battlecruisers *Renown* and *Repulse* of 1914 was as follows;

PRIVATE YARDS:

Armstrong	7
(including 3 ordered by foreign governments)	
Beardmore	4
John Brown	5
Cammell Laird	1
Fairfield	4
Palmers	4
Scotts	2
Thames Iron Works	1
Vickers	7
(including 3 ordered by foreign governments)	

ROYAL DOCKYARDS:

Devonport	10
Portsmouth	7

Conqueror awaiting sea trials, is flanked by the Warilda *(left) and the* Wandilla *in July 1912. The cruiser* Dublin *is fitting-out at the other side of the basin.*

So rapid was the growth of the battleship in size and offensive power during this short period, that an interesting comparison can be made between the *Agamemnon* and the *Ramillies*.

	AGAMEMNON 1904	RAMILLIES 1913
Deep load displacement	17,683 tons	33,000 tons
Length overall	443.5 feet	624.25 feet
Main armament	Four 12 inch	Eight 15 inch
Machinery	Triple expansion 16,750 ihp	Steam turbines 40,000 shp
Speed	18 knots	21.5 knots

Opposite top. The Allan liner Alsatian, heeling slightly to starboard, passes the berth she was built on following dry docking at Govan in November or December 1913. The years immediately before the war were exceptionally busy as this photograph illustrates. The stern of the Benbow, *recently launched from the gantry, can be seen in the fitting-out basin while every building berth is occupied. Note the light coloured destroyer on an improvised berth out of alignment with the main berths. This photograph was taken from John Brown's yard which has acquired covered building berths as seen in the foreground.*

There were two notable launches in 1913. The first, in March, was the *Alsatian*, the largest passenger ship so far built at Dalmuir. The second and more impressive was that of the battleship *Benbow* launched by Lady Randolph Churchill on 12 November. On this occasion, A J Campbell made a gesture which did much to dramatise the proportions as well as the urgency of the naval shipbuilding programme then underway. A 100 foot long, 30 ton keel section of the new battleship *Ramillies* was hoisted to the top of the shipbuilding gantry above the hull of the *Benbow* and ceremoniously lowered into position on the berth when that ship was launched. This combined launching and keel laying took twenty minutes to perform. Construction of the *Benbow* to launching stage had been subject to considerable delay taking 18 months in contrast to the 9 months for sister vessels building in the Royal Dockyards. In his after launch speech, Beardmore attributed this to 'labour disputes, short time working, the coal strike and the scarcity of labour'. The coal strike had disrupted production for three or four months after which it had been very difficult to take on sufficient men to build the *Benbow*. This had resulted in wages being increased which in turn, Beardmore was sad to say. 'had the effect of greatly delaying the work'. According to Beardmore, men had begun to 'slacken off work and put in very short time . . .'[10]

In 1913, what were to be the last merchant orders to be taken for some time were placed. The first was the 900 ton lighthouse tender *Nearchus* for the Royal Indian Marine which was launched on 18 November 1914, the second, a 16,000 ton passenger liner to be named *Conte Rosso* for the Lloyd Sabaudo Line of Genoa. The latter ship was laid down in June 1914 and was expected to enter

Opposite bottom. In July 1914, the King and Queen visited Dalmuir arriving in the fitting-out basin by paddle steamer. The Royal party can be seen rounding the after 13.5 inch turrets of the battleship Benbow.

service on the New York-Genoa run in 1916. The declaration of War two months later caused an immediate suspension of work on this ship and what there was of her occupied an important building berth for the next two years before her future was determined.

1913 was the year of record achievement for Clyde shipbuilders and the UK in general. Dalmuir produced its highest output to date and second highest throughout the period of the yard's existence. At 44,435 tons it was nevertheless well behind John Brown at 82,722 tons and Armstrong at 99,333 tons.

On 19 December, the *Alsatian* completed successful steam and manoeuvring trials on the Firth of Clyde making one knot in excess of her contract speed. This well appointed ship was built in the comparatively short period of twenty two months from keel laying. While on the final trial run of the *Alsatian*, William Beardmore, looking to the future, stated his intention to add submarine construction and aero engine manufacture to his firm's activities. In fact as events were to prove, these developments would form only a small part of the new areas in which his Company would become involved. Profitability however, had eluded the Dalmuir works every year until the outbreak of war with the exception of minor profits made during 1910 and 1911.

Nevertheless, on the eve of the Great War, William Beardmore had indeed succeeded in his aim of establishing his Company alongside Armstrong and Vickers, as one of the leading armaments manufacturers and warship builders in the United Kingdom. In addition to the creation of the Naval Construction Works at Dalmuir, large steel works at Mossend in Lanarkshire had been acquired in 1905, modernised and extended to provide the shipyard with steel plate and sections. The forge at Parkhead had been equipped to enable the manufacture of the largest calibres of naval and other ordnance while a new armour plate mill commissioned in 1913, was at the time the largest in existence.

Now, when the 'maximum demand' – for which Beardmore had so optimistically planned years earlier – was about to be placed on his firm, he stood in a position second to none to meet the needs of a country at war. In recognition of his efforts to date, Beardmore was made a Baronet in April 1914. At a presentation given in his honour in Glasgow, Sir William was presented with a

large illuminated address designed by artists employed by the firm. The address was signed by 5,000 employees and included the following statement;

> 'We, the members of the staff and workmen employed by Messrs. William Beardmore & Co., take this opportunity of conveying to you our warm appreciation of your character as a man and an employer and of those qualities of strong unswerving courage and lofty enterprise, together with that kindly consideration and generous recognition of merit in others, which mark you out as a veritable captain of industry. That continued success attend you and long life and happiness be granted to you and your good lady, Lady Beardmore, is our earnest wish and prayer'[11]

Royal endorsement in the form of a works visit followed on 14 July when King George V and Queen Mary visited the Beardmore works at Parkhead and Dalmuir. Sailing down river from Glasgow by paddle steamer, the Royal party arrived in the fitting-out basin at the Naval Construction Works to moor alongside the battleship *Benbow*,

then nearing completion. The King and Queen were led across the battleship's quarterdeck to pause beneath the twin 13.5 inch gun barrels of 'Y' turret – the supreme symbols of British seapower to which William Beardmore and his Company had become inextricably linked.

The King, accompanied by Sir William, walks round the quarterdeck of the Benbow.

The handsome Allan liner Alsatian running trials in December 1913. The Alsatian became the Empress of France in 1919 when the Allan Line was taken over by Canadian Pacific Steamships. She ended her life at Dalmuir in 1934/35 being broken-up in the basin where she was completed 21 years before.

THE GREAT WAR: 1914 – 1918

On the outbreak of war in August 1914, the Naval Construction Works at Dalmuir became committed to the manufacture of a very wide range of war materials, in addition to shipbuilding, for which the Works was only partly prepared. Although shipbuilding continued to be the most significant activity, the new demands including field guns, howitzers, aircraft and airships, required the creation of new shops and facilities for which there was ample space within existing yard boundaries. In the case of airships however, the scale of construction was so vast that a new site at Inchinnan was found where an extremely large airship hangar and other shops were erected. The construction of submarines had already been anticipated and the first phase of the new submarine yard was well in hand by the start of the war.

During the war years the Admiralty understandably placed great demands upon the warship building yards which they had carefully nurtured in preceding years. One of the greatest challenges facing these yards was the ability to respond rapidly to naval requirements as the priorities of the war at sea changed. Generally there was little need to order further battleships in 1914, as it was clear that when the ships of the Iron Duke, Queen Elizabeth and Revenge Classes were completed, the Royal Navy would enjoy an overwhelming superiority over the German fleet of 34 to 19 battleships and battlecruisers.

However, lack of numbers in other warship types was quickly made evident, perhaps the most pressing of which was the need for more destroyers to screen the battleships of the Grand Fleet. The deficiency in numbers of large ocean going submarines was addressed by events described later, while the apparent need to have submarines capable of fleet speed led to the steam driven 'K' class being given priority from 1915 onwards. The

Newspaper boys waiting at the main gate on Beardmore Street for the works hooter to go on the 16th October 1916 – the day the battleship Ramillies was launched.

early successes of German light cruisers and armed merchant cruisers against British shipping led to the design and laying down of large, light cruisers of great endurance (Hawkins Class). However, such were the vagaries of the sea war, that by the end of 1916 this threat had been countered and the construction of these cruisers was decelerated.

The Dalmuir works participated in all of these programmes in what stands out as the busiest period of the yard's existence. On hand at the outbreak of war were two battleships, three light cruisers, two submarines, a lighthouse tender and the incomplete hull of the suspended Italian liner *Conte Rosso*.

BATTLESHIPS

In August 1914, British superiority in battleship numbers was largely on paper as the newest and most powerful units were still building. Consequently there was great urgency attached to the completion of ships still in builders' hands and

work on the *Benbow* which was almost complete, proceeded with some speed. By October she was ready for trials. On 1 December, she sailed from the Clyde to Berehaven in Southern Ireland to 'work-up'. After a further brief trials period, she sailed north on 10 December to join the Fourth Battle Squadron of the Grand Fleet at Scapa Flow although an element of fitting-out was still in progress.

The much larger battleship *Ramillies*, laid down in November 1913, had, for reasons outwith Beardmore's control, the longest building time of all British battleships despite the original contract stipulation of 24 months. This delay – she took 43 months from keel laying to trials – highlights two areas in which the emergency war building programme was subjected to severe strain; the shortage of skilled workers, especially platers and riveters, and the difficulties encountered by the armaments companies in coping with the great demand for main armament mountings.

Although there were simply not enough workers to meet the demands placed on the shipyards, once they were declared controlled establishments in 1915, the Admiralty was able to direct and control labour through the Admiralty Priority Section and, to some extent, regulate the supply of labour to individual yards. In February 1917, this section was absorbed into the Shipyard Labour Department whose task was to co-ordinate the supply of labour to the private yards and engineering works engaged in naval and merchant work.[1] In September/October 1915 for example, a large number of ironworkers were taken off the *Ramillies* at Dalmuir and directed up-river to work on the urgently required battlecruiser *Renown* building at Fairfield.[2] While there was little that could be done to increase the pool of skilled labour, every effort was made to increase production from those that were available. Weekend working appeared for a time to offer every prospect of achieving this objective as

Saturday afternoon working was paid at one and a half times the hourly or piece rate and Sunday working twice. However, during 1915 it was found that the undoubted popularity of weekend working, along with the increase in output it provided, was offset in many cases by a nearly equal amount of time taken off during the week when normal rates applied. This experience whereby output remained much the same while

Below. The battleship is launched unfortunately hitting the bottom as she enters the water causing serious damage to her stern.

Ramillies is manoeuvred into the fitting-out basin after launching. Her funnel together with 'B' or 'X' barbette has already been built and awaits fitting under the hammerhead crane. The relative proximity of the Inchinnan airship works on the south side of the Clyde is evidenced by the airship shed which is just visible above the trees over the battleship's stern.

costs had risen, effectively stopped weekend working.[3]

The manufacture of gun mountings was the other major bottleneck. With only a few firms capable of their design and construction, the volume of orders on hand at the start of the war placed almost intolerable demands on their ability to fulfil them. No fewer than twelve capital ships were building requiring a total of 46 twin 15 inch mountings (not including those needed for monitors and large cruisers). To complicate matters, it was decided in December 1914, that two of these vessels – the *Renown* and *Repulse* – should be built at great speed in a *tour de force* of British shipbuilding prowess reminiscent of the rapid building of the *Dreadnought* eight years previously. The motivating force behind this was Lord Fisher once more installed as First Sea Lord of the Admiralty. Fisher, impressed by the success of British battlecruisers, in the hunting down and destruction of Von Spee's squadron off the Falklands, was convinced of the need to see further ships of this type in service. To speed the building of the *Renown* and *Repulse*, the 15 inch mountings intended for the *Ramillies* were diverted to them and to the monitors *Marshal Ney* and *Marshal Soult*. In a note to the shipyard dated 9 February 1916, the Admiralty advised Beardmore that new mountings for the *Ramillies* would not now be

delivered until December of that year. As the *Ramillies* was going to be late in service, the opportunity was taken to modify her design by 'bulging' the battleship while she lay on the stocks on condition that completion, now projected well into 1917, was not further delayed. 'Bulging' referred to the external fitting of anti-torpedo bulges to either side of the ship's hull in an attempt to render the main structure of the hull and vitals enclosed, more secure from the explosive effect of a torpedo hit. The bulges covered about three quarters of the ship's length and projected outboard about seven feet. The battleship's original beam of 88.5 feet now became 101.5 feet which made her a rather tight fit under the shipbuilding gantry which had clearance of only 105 feet. To expedite work on the anti-torpedo bulges, the Admiralty requested the Fairfield yard to return the workers lent from Dalmuir on October of the previous year.[4]

The total cost of fitting anti-torpedo bulges to the battleship came to almost £168,000. As a consequence of this considerable additional building work, the *Ramillies* was not launched until 12 October 1916 when Lady Jackson, wife of Admiral Sir Henry Jackson, then the First Sea Lord, performed the ceremony. Launching, perhaps the most hazardous event undertaken by any ship, was to be marred by a serious mishap. On

An illustration of the Ramillies on completion in 1917.

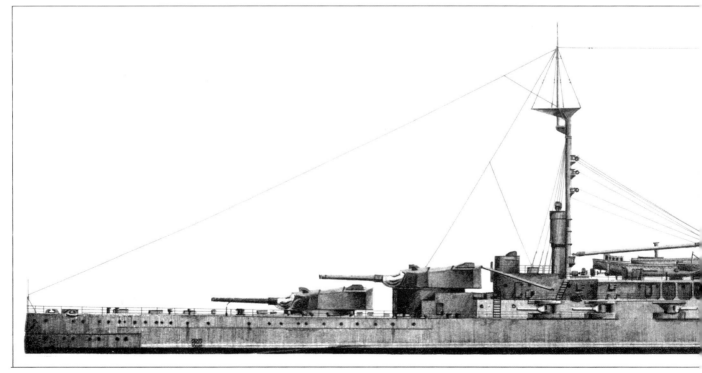

her passage down the slipway into the Clyde, the *Ramillies* hit the bottom causing extensive damage to her rudders and plating in the vicinity of the stern. Immediate repair was not possible as there was no dry dock large enough to accommodate her on the Clyde and, in any case, she was not in a sinking condition despite some minor flooding to compartments in the vicinity of the damage. The lack of a suitable dry dock was somewhat ironic in this instance in view of William Beardmore's early, if unfulfilled, recognition that a large dry dock would be an important part of Dalmuir shipyard.

At least part of the reason for the launching accident can be attributed to the launch weight of the battleship which at 18,750 tons was far in excess of her four sister ships none of which went into the water at a weight greater than 12,000 tons. Some of this extra weight can be accounted for by the addition of the bulges and the fact that at least part of the main armour belt, which had to be fitted before the bulges were complete, was already fitted contrary to normal practice.

Subsequently, a Board of Enquiry was established to investigate the cause of the incident and to determine if there was any neglect on the part of the builder. Launching calculations were investigated, slipway supports were examined and the state and time of tides checked but no evidence of neglect on the part of Beardmore could be found and the matter was finally dropped.[5]

On completion in May 1917, as a consequence of her damaged stern, the *Ramillies* had what must be one of the most unfortunate passages down river of any new ship leaving the Clyde. As inspection and repair of the damaged area was essential, the ship had to be taken to the Gladstone dry dock at Liverpool, the nearest available dock where this could be carried out. In splendid ignorance of what was to follow, preparations were in hand to commission the battleship into the navy. Three hundred officers and men of the crew, already assigned to the ship and living in Dalmuir Hall during the fitting-out period, were joined by a further 500 men who arrived by train from Devonport at 9 am on the morning of 7 May for the commissioning ceremony. After the ceremony and with six tugs in attendance, the *Ramillies* left Dalmuir at 2 pm to the cheers of thousands while overhead an aircraft looped the loop. Shortly after passing Dumbarton Rock, the battleship suddenly sheered out of line and ran aground. After desperate efforts by the tugs she was pulled off after an hour and the journey restarted. Off Gourock she ran aground again, this time in mid channel, and lay there with the tide ebbing, like the proverbial stranded whale as the receding water uncovered her anti-torpedo bulges.

At 2.30 a.m. the following morning she was pulled free and dropped anchor in deeper water. On 10 May departure to Liverpool was again attempted but the vessel became so unmanoueverable that 'she drifted more or less broadside on through the anti-submarine gate' hitting a trawler in the process. The following day 'bowler hatted experts from Beardmore's arrived on board to review the situation and decided to rapidly manufacture and fit steel manoeuvring levers, nicknamed 'whiskers', at either side of the ship's hull aft to give more leverage to the lines attached from the tugs. Before this work could be carried out, another abortive attempt at moving the ship was tried, this time by steering with the engines only. Finally, on 23 May, the *Ramillies*, complete with newly fitted 'whiskers' projecting from the side, left the Clyde. Ever mindful of the submarine threat, the ship was accompanied by no less than eight minesweepers, eight Liverpool tugs, eight trawlers and six destroyers. Once underway, the tug masters refused to use the levers as they considered them dangerous and so the *Ramillies* was towed, or more

likely dragged, to Liverpool at a speed of four knots.[6] She docked on 25 May and following repairs, joined the First Battle Squadron of the Grand Fleet at Scapa Flow in September 1917.

The Company books for 1918 record the sum of £1,083 against repairs to the ship's bottom and £6,179 against repairs to the rudders and sternpost.

AIRCRAFT CARRIER

One of the most interesting and significant vessels to appear during the First World War period was the *Argus*, the world's first flush-deck aircraft carrier. This ship began life at Dalmuir in June 1914 as the Italian liner *Conte Rosso* building for the Lloyd Sabaudo Line of Genoa. When hostilities commenced in August of that year work on the ship – which had not reached a very advanced state – was suspended.

The early development of an aircraft carrying ship in which the Beardmore Company was heavily involved, pre-dates the laying down of the *Conte Rosso* by several years when a design for a 'parent ship for naval aeroplanes' was prepared by the

Company at the behest of the Marquis of Graham. The first proposal, submitted to the Admiralty on 23 October 1912, was for a vessel with a flat deck running the length of the hull. Hangars for a total of six seaplanes were arranged down either side of the deck. This vessel had a length of 450 feet and an overall breadth of 110 feet and was capable of a speed of 21 knots in order to keep station with the fleet. Following discussions with Captain Murray Sueter and Rear Admiral Moore, both of whom were firm believers in the use of aircraft at sea, this design was modified and a second proposal was drawn up for a slightly smaller vessel of 15 knots speed it being considered by naval personnel that there would be no requirement for this ship to accompany the fleet. This proposal, which ran to a very detailed 110 page specification together with plans, was submitted to the Admiralty on 19 December 1912. (See Appendix 11). Following serious consideration of the proposal, the Admiralty decided not to proceed further citing the great breadth of the carrier as an undesirable aspect of the design.

These early proposals are of some importance in light of the future status of the aircraft carrier. Writing in 1927 for *Beardmore News*, the Company magazine, TNS Dickson, chief ship designer at Dalmuir said of the October 1912 proposal-

'the first design of this vessel was prepared and sent to the Admiralty in 1912/13, when in conjunction with the Marquis of Graham we prepared a design for a vessel 450 feet long and 21 knots speed capable of carrying six hydroplanes fully extended and ready for flight in hangars on each side of the vessel with a central platform screened by the hangars all fore and aft to enable planes to take off. The vessel also carried additional seaplanes which could be assembled to replace those damaged or lost in action. The original had a raising and lowering platform at the after end, from the poop to the waterline and electric capstans for drawing the seaplanes aboard as they were supposed to alight on water. In addition to this however, cranes were also supplied for lifting them aboard. (In those days, of course, there was no talk of folding wings or other devices because they too were in their infancy otherwise a large number could have been carried). The design was very favourably received by the Admiralty but as the usual outcry for economy in expenditure was in full force, it was decided not to proceed any further with this matter'

Nevertheless, there was continued and growing interest in ships of this type and by early 1916, the desirability of operating aircraft at sea was fully recognised. So rapid was the development of aircraft, that proposals to operate seaplanes soon gave way to flying wheeled aircraft from flight decks. As a means of having such a vessel at sea relatively quickly, the conversion of a suitable merchant hull with high enough speed seemed promising and two such hulls were identified one of which was the *Conte Rosso* at Dalmuir. In 1916, the works General Manager, A J Campbell, wrote to the Admiralty with reference to that vessel saying that Beardmore owed the Lloyd Sabaudo Line £127,288 which had been received for work done on the ship up until suspension and that this sum would have to be repaid. He further stated that work on the ship's machinery was well advanced and approximately 1,100 tons of material had been worked into the vessel while a further 4,344 tons of plates and 1,750 tons of sections had been delivered to the yard. Campbell ended with 'might we point out to their Lordships that this vessel has occupied a valuable berth for two years and its release would be a very valuable asset'[7]

In August 1916, the Company was informed by the Admiralty that if work did proceed it would be on the condition that work on other Admiralty contracts in the yard should not be interrupted and that in particular work should not interfere with 'the most rapid progress possible of the K boat' (steam driven submarine *K17*). On 20 September 1916, the First Sea Lord made the decision to proceed and the yard was officially notified to that effect on 6 October, the work to

The Argus on trials on the Firth of Clyde in 1918 wearing an Admiralty disruptive camouflage scheme. In fleet service she was referred to as the 'flat iron'.

be undertaken with all dispatch to ensure completion by 1 November 1917.[8] However progress on the *Argus*, as the ship was renamed, was not to be so quick partly because of uncertainty as to the configuration of her flight deck and in particular the arrangement of her bridges and funnels. As initially designed she resembled the original Beardmore hydroplane carrier of 1912 in that she was to have twin islands one on either side of the flight deck with a bridge spanning these islands under which aircraft would pass. Wind tunnel tests of this arrangement carried out at the National Physical Laboratory from November 1916 onwards, indicated that this structure would be less than satisfactory subjecting the flight deck to severe turbulence. The *Argus* was launched on the 2 September 1917 and taken to the basin for completion where it seems likely that twin islands were indeed fitted to the flight deck. However, these were subsequently removed as the findings of the National Physical Laboratory were reinforced by tests carried out in the summer of 1917 on the converted large cruiser *Furious* which retained most of her superstructure aft of a forward flying-off deck. The islands were removed and *Argus* was completed in September 1918 with a flush deck, the first true aircraft carrier. Of this ship TNS Dickson said —

> 'In order to give this vessel a flying deck entirely free from obstruction the funnels were carried horizontally between the flying deck and the top of the hangar. These were carried right aft and fitted with large fans to ensure satisfactory draught even with a following wind. The charthouse was made to raise and lower hydraulically. A proposal was made to grow grass on the flight deck but, as this meant an addition of about 300 tons at this level, was not pressed. The general appearance of the vessel was somewhat grotesque, rather in the nature of a furniture removal van sharpened at the fore end'.

It is not entirely clear to what extent the Beardmore Company contributed or influenced original ideas in the design of the Argus, but there can be little doubt that the October 1912 design was indeed a very far sighted initiative. In 1927 the Duke of Montrose (until 1925 the Marquis of Graham) submitted the following letter as part of a claim to the Royal Commission on Awards to Inventors under the clear belief that his ideas had been instrumental in the evolution of the aircraft carrier.

'Claim in respect of idea, design, planning and arrangements for an ocean going naval aircraft carrier for operating with a fleet at sea.

This claim is made in general that I am the originator or inventor of the idea of a fast ocean going ship to carry aircraft at sea and from which aircraft could work and return. Also that such a ship should provide means for repairs stowage of fuel, bombs, spare parts and living quarters for naval airmen. This claim is made in particular that I worked out these plans and had them drawn in outline on the 23 October 1912 by Messrs Wm Beardmore & Co and submitted them to the Admiralty. They were considered of value and the Admiralty appointed a committee to go into them with me, the Admiralty representatives being Rear Admiral Moore and Captain Murray Sueter RN. As a result of several meetings with these officers, it was arranged that I would prepare a detailed set of plans and have them drawn out with complete specifications and this I did with Messrs Wm Beardmore & Co and I finally lodged them with the Admiralty on 19 December 1912. These plans were accepted by the Admiralty and treated as confidential papers and constituted the only design the Admiralty possessed on the outbreak of War for an ocean going aircraft carrier. In 1916 when HMS Argus was ordered from Messrs Wm Beardmore & Co Ltd, my plans were taken out, studied, and many of the ideas approved and embodied in the designs for that vessel but I have never personally received directly or indirectly any recognition financial or otherwise in respect of my idea, work, and plans for an ocean aircraft carrier. I can support this claim by producing copies of plans and specifications of my submission in 1912 which, compared with the plans and specifications of HMS Argus, will show exactly the ideas of mine which have been embodied in the plans for the latter. I can also support my claim by evidence from Admiral Sueter and the naval designers of Wm Beardmore & Co that my plans were original, were thought out by me, and had never been utilised or known before. The delay in submitting this claim is due to the fact that Messrs Wm Beardmore & Co had other claims against the Admiralty and it was considered undesirable that, being a director of Wm Beardmore & Co, I should concurrently submit this which is a personal claim. As I understand it, the Inventions Committee will shortly terminate their work. I have considered it undesirable to delay submission any longer.[9]

The Admiralty were not inclined to accept this view, and on 2 August 1927 replied to the Duke's solicitor,

Sir,

with reference to your letter of 22 June 1927 relative to a claim by the Duke of Montrose in respect of his invention of aerial motor carriages on ships, I have to inform you that it cannot be admitted that the Admiralty are indebted to the Duke of Montrose for the design of aircraft carriers in HM service. On 19 December 1912 as a result of interviews between naval officers and representatives of Messrs Wm Beardmore & Co Ltd, the firm submitted to the Admiralty for their consideration, a design for a proposed parent ship for naval aeroplanes and torpedo boat destroyers together with plans, specifications and an estimate of the time required to build and complete such a vessel in the event of an order being placed. The design was for a vessel in which seaplanes were stowed in hangars at the side of the flying deck which had a clear run fore and aft between the hangars. This necessitated great width at the flying deck which was considered the chief objection to the design. The matter was dropped and Messrs Beardmore informed in April 1913 that sufficient experience had not been gained with hydroplanes working from a ship at sea to enable naval requirements in this direction to be definitely stated and in these circumstances the Admiralty did not deem it advisable to proceed further with the matter at that time. The details of the design of Argus were worked out by Messrs Beardmore in 1916 to meet Admiralty requirements. This design differed essentially from that submitted by the Firm in 1912 the flying deck being built above the deck and lifts installed to transport the aircraft between the flight deck and the hangars and the

The light cruiser Galatea *shortly before launching on 14 May 1914.*

Less than two months later, on 6 July 1914, Galatea's sister ship Inconstant *is launched by Princess Louise of Battenberg.*

The completed light cruiser Galatea – the first British warship to spot elements of the German High Seas Fleet immediately prior to the Battle of Jutland in May 1916.

While placing the hangars below the flight deck does indeed constitute a different design solution from that proposed in the 1912 design, the above letter surely misses the point. The notion of placing hangars in close proximity to a flying-off platform, whether beside or below, established a concept which enabled a series of further and improved designs to evolve.

CRUISERS

The light-scout cruisers *Galatea*, *Inconstant* and *Royalist* of the Arethusa Class were completed early in the war, the last of the three, *Royalist*, running trials towards the end of March 1915. The *Galatea* achieved a degree of fame as being the British warship which first signalled the presence of the High Seas Fleet at the outset of the Battle of Jutland on 31 May 1916.

The only other cruiser to be built at Dalmuir during the war period was the 10,000 ton light cruiser *Raleigh* of the Hawkins class although she was destined not to be completed for almost six years. Laid down in December 1915 to meet the threat of German commerce raiders, work on the *Raleigh* proceeded at a leisurely pace once this threat became less pressing. Completed in 1921, she had a very brief operational career, grounding off the coast of Labrador in 1922 becoming a constructive total loss.

DESTROYERS

In addition to the *Goshawk*, *Lennox* and *Llewellyn* which were completed before the war, orders for

funnel gases were led through horizontal ducts between the flying deck and the hangar roof. For their work on Argus, Messrs Beardmore were paid. The extent to which the Duke of Montrose was concerned in the proposals put forward by Messrs Beardmore in 1912, is not known to the Admiralty, the official negotiations having been conducted between the Admiralty and the firm, who do not appear to have made any claim. The essential features of the 1912 design have not been adopted in any aircraft carriers built for the Admiralty.

I am your obedient servant,
GB Cobb
for Director of Navy Contracts[10]

a total of twenty-two destroyers of various classes were received. This reflected the shortage of this type of warship at the commencement of hostilities. The demand for destroyers was essentially two-fold; to provide adequate escorts for the heavy ships of the Grand Fleet, the shortage of which had caused Admiral Jellicoe to make repeated and urgent requests to the Admiralty for the acceleration of the destroyer programme, and secondly, to provide sufficient destroyers to tackle the U-Boats which, although always perceived as a serious menace, looked as if they might, in 1917, succeed in their objective of blockading the British Isles.

In response, destroyers were laid down wherever a large enough space could be found at the berths. In 1918, three V and W class destroyers were built simultaneously under the shipbuilding gantry. Of the twenty-two destroyers ordered from the Company, five were cancelled at the end of the war and broken-up on the berths. Two of these were initially shifted to clear an important berth and re-erected on other slips after approximately £75,000 had been spent on them. £80,000 had been spent on the *Daring* and an unknown amount on the *Vimy*, before notice of cancellation was received from the Admiralty. The machinery for these vessels, which was at various stages of completion, was dismantled. The fifth destroyer, *Desperate*, appears not to have been laid down.

Two other destroyers, *Nizam* and *Pylades*, which were launched at Alexander Stephens yard at Linthouse in 1916, were completed at Dalmuir later that year.

SUBMARINES

William Beardmore's interest and involvement

As the war proceeded the need for destroyers became paramount. Here the destroyers Tactician, Tara *and* Tasmania *are building simultaneously under the gantry in the spring of 1918.*

*Right. The V and W Class
destroyer* Vancouver *leaving
Dalmuir in March 1918.*

*Below. The Laforey Class
destroyer* Lassoo *which was
completed in October 1915
and sunk after hitting a mine
in August 1916.*

*Bottom. The S Class
destroyer* Tasmania *on trials
on the Firth of Clyde early in
1919. She was transferred to
the Royal Australian Navy in
June of that year.*

in the construction of submarines preceded the
war and was not in response to the Emergency
War Programme. As this resulted in the building
of a purpose-built submarine yard at Dalmuir
before 1914, it is worth looking briefly at the
development of submarine building in this
country up to that time.

The history of modern submarine building in
the United Kingdom is short, dating back to an
agreement made in December 1900 – at the behest
of the Admiralty – between the Electric Boat
Company of New York, builders of the successful
Holland submarines for the United States' Navy,
and Vickers Son and Maxim at Barrow. By this
agreement, Vickers would build Holland boats

for the Royal Navy under license. After five boats were built, a new agreement was drawn-up between the Admiralty and Vickers which gave that Company almost exclusive rights to the building of submarines in this country and allowed them to become the sole designers of new types derived from experience gained from the operation of Holland boats. However, in an effort to broaden experience in this very specialised activity, the Admiralty, between 1907 and 1909, placed a series of submarine orders with Chatham Dockyard. This arrangement lasted until March 1911 when the Admiralty, now anxious to involve other private firms, terminated the agreement with Vickers, although under the terms of the agreement, two years were still to run.

Two other firms, Armstrong Whitworth and Scotts, had begun building submarines of French and Italian design before the war for evaluation by the Admiralty, although they were not completed until after 1915. On the outbreak of war therefore, the only yards which had any practical experience of submarine construction resulting in boats actually being completed, were Vickers and Chatham Dockyard. In late 1912, Beardmore, aware of the Admiralty's desire to involve other firms in submarine construction, decided to press ahead with the building of a submarine yard at Dalmuir, in the hope that his enterprise would be rewarded. Beardmore had tried to break the Vickers monopoly and establish submarine building facilities at Dalmuir as early as 1907. This scheme embraced four covered building slips in a shed 210 feet long by 180 feet wide, each berth served by an overhead travelling crane of five tons lift. As this yard – also used for the building of other small vessels in the absence of submarine contracts – was on the other side of the fitting-out basin from the main yard, a separate platers shed and stores complex was built adjacent to the new berths. By 1913, two of the four berths were constructed followed later by the other two which were not completed until 1917. The sheds were built by Sir William Arrol and Company.

Curiously, Beardmore's first submarine order came, not from the Admiralty but from Vickers who had received an order on 29 April 1914 from the Turkish Government to build several warships including two submarines of similar design to the British 'E' class. As Vickers had no berths available to lay them down, the orders were sub-contracted to Beardmore.

Left. Beardmore's first submarine E25 ready for launching from the submarine sheds in August 1915.

Below. Fifty six E Class submarines were built of which Beardmore built four. This is E54 running trials during 1916.

In October 1914, Lord Fisher, the former First Sea Lord, was reinstated in his old position and lost no time in rectifying what he considered, among other things, to be a neglect of the submarine service, which had resulted in too few long range boats being built. On 11 November 1914, a conference was held at the Admiralty with various shipbuilders in attendance in order to determine the maximum number of existing submarine types that could be put in hand. Decisions were made rapidly and by the end of the day a total of 38 submarine orders were placed with 12 different builders.[11] Beardmore was given four boats to build which included the two Turkish boats referred to as 'already building' and which had been requisitioned by the Government on the outbreak of war.

For the firms with no experience in submarine work, and this meant nearly all, the drawings and patterns of the hull castings, conning tower and other large casings were made available at Chatham Dockyard. Two submarines nearing completion

Top. The steam driven fleet submarine K16, in the fitting-out basin at Dalmuir on 12 April 1918.

were also made available for inspection. To save time in construction, the above mentioned parts together with the main engines, periscopes, periscope brackets, steering and hydroplane gear, motors pumps, compressors, Kingston valves etc, were ordered directly by the Admiralty.[12]

In this manner, submarine building commenced in various yards throughout the country. At Dalmuir, a total of eleven submarines of the E, L, H and K classes were ordered during the war years and of these, the *L59* and *L70* were cancelled after the Armistice. Several of the boats on order were not completed until after the war ended. Following the launch of *L69* in 1918, she was towed to Devonport Dockyard where construction continued slowly until completion in 1923. The Fairfield launched submarines *E47* and *E48* were completed at Dalmuir in 1917.

OTHER VESSELS

At the beginning of the War when the Dardanelles campaign was under consideration, it was evident that a large number of landing craft would be required to transport the troops ashore in what was to be the first large scale amphibious operation ever mounted. With some urgency, a large number of small craft were ordered from various builders. At Dalmuir, twenty X Lighters – 105 foot long diesel driven landing craft – were built on every suitable scrap of land that could be found. Ordered in February 1915, most had been launched by

mid-summer and delivered in August of the same year. An order for twelve 'dumb' barges (not engined) was also received that year.

Four hospital paddle ships *HP4*, *5*, *6* and *7* and two paddle transport ships *P50* and *P51* were built for service in the Mesopotamian theatre.

In addition to the many warships built at Dalmuir during the war, many others were overhauled or repaired, including the pre-dreadnought battleships *Hannibal*, *Mars* and *Magnificent*. Smaller vessels included the *Crescent*, *Gloucester*, *Porpoise*, *Hardy* (twice), *Bristol*, *Hope*, *Carysfort*, *Crane*, *Dahlia*, *Foxglove*, *Godetia*, *Gentian*, *Marigold*, *K17*, *N1*, *L3* and *L4*.[13]

As well as the machinery and boilers built for ships on order, the Engine and Boiler Shops turned out the following; four Yarrow boilers of 12,000 hp each for installation in four 'P' class paddle steamers building at Caird's yard in Greenock. Eight cylindrical boilers of 1,000 hp each for 'standard' ships building in various yards; the machinery for the destroyer *Nomad* building at Alexander Stephens. Two 8 cylinder oil engines for 'E' class submarines, three 12 cylinder oil engines for 'L' class submarines and 63 sets of trawler engines.

SHIPBUILDING OUTPUT 1914 – 1918

The total number of ships, including landing craft and barges, built at the Naval Construction Works at Dalmuir during the war period, amounted to seventy three vessels of 120,000 tons. Machinery output came to a total of 687,000 hp. In both areas, this was the third highest output on Clydeside after John Brown and Fairfield. These figures might well have been higher had it not been that two out of the six berths in the main yard were effectively out of commission for long periods due to lack of progress on the *Ramillies* and *Conte Rosso*, a disadvantage not suffered to the same extent by the other two Clyde yards[14]. Although the yard was exceptionally busy throughout this period, space was apparently available for laying down a large battlecruiser in the early months of 1915. In a letter to the Director of Naval Construction dated 6 March, Lord Fisher states that 'Beardmore and Vickers are absolutely sure they can produce two ships in eleven months'[15]. The vessels referred to were the product of Fisher's desire to mount the largest guns – in this case 20 inch – on large lightly armoured but fast hulls. The vessels were never ordered; Fisher left the Admiralty and the project was dropped.

The weekly wage bill at Dalmuir rose at one point to £47,700 in contrast to the average weekly wage bill of £14,800 for 1914.[16] Precise wartime employment figures are unknown for the shipyard

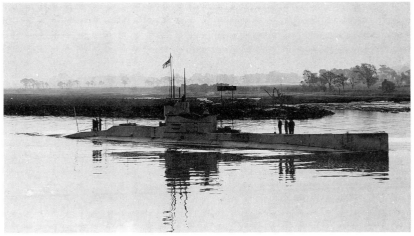

The L Class submarine L6 passing Newshot Isle on her way to run trials in 1918.

although according to A J Campbell, the highest prewar figure was 13,000 and it seems more than likely that this would have been exceeded during the war. Another source gives the 1914 figure as 5,854 and the 1917 figure as 10,855 although this may be for the shipyard department alone.[17] The magnitude of the Beardmore wartime empire can be gauged by the following statistics; the total number of employees in various works rose from a prewar low of 10,080 to 42,500 in 1918, the weekly wage bill rising from £22,888 to £145,000 in the corresponding period.[18]

The conflicting objectives of providing men for the front while increasing production for the war effort, was partly offset by the introduction of women workers into the factories under the

The hospital paddle ship HP5 on the Clyde. These ships, intended for river operation, had very low freeboard and had to have wooden sides added in order to make the voyage to the middle east. They were designed by the leading Glasgow naval architect Sir Percy Biles.

Women workers at Dalmuir in 1918.

Posing in the lower half of a mine

dilution scheme. The Clyde Commission for the Dilution of Labour was formally constituted on 22nd January 1916, although by that time no fewer than 14,000 women had already been placed in 150 out of 300 large 'controlled' works in the Clyde area.[19] Facilities for the new labour force were hastily built during 1916 including a 'dining room and cloakroom for women' adjacent to the engine and field gun shops

The exact number of women employed at Dalmuir is unknown. In November 1916, *Engineering* listed the following operations undertaken by women in shipyards; cleaning out machine shops, stores and offices; attending light drilling machines; red leading and rough painting and labouring for joiners and carpenters – 'all with satisfactory results'.

AIRCRAFT AND AIRSHIPS

The sudden demand for aircraft brought about by the outbreak of war in 1914, forced the Government to seek additional manufacturing capacity outwith the embryonic aircraft industry already established in Britain. The choice fell on engineering firms who, if not already familiar with actual aircraft construction techniques, could be relied on to rapidly acquire them.

On Clydeside a number of shipbuilding and engineering firms, including Beardmore, participated in this scheme under the overall control of Lord Weir who was appointed Director of Munitions in Scotland in 1915 and later, in

1917, Controller of Aeronautical Supplies.[20] Unlike most other firms however, Beardmore's interest in aviation had preceded the outbreak of war in much the same way that submarines had. Typically, William Beardmore had been attracted by the possibilities of powered flight and at about the same time that his Company was talking to the Admiralty about hydroplane carriers, he acquired the British manufacturing rights to the German DFW biplane. Two aircraft of diferent design – a seaplane and a landplane were brought over from Germany and assembled by Beardmore in 1914 although the landplane was never completed. Simultaneously, manufacturing rights to the Austro Daimler 120 hp aero engine were acquired and production facilities created at the Arrol Johnston motor works at Dumfries in which Beardmore had become the major shareholder in 1902. By May 1914, 90 and 120 hp versions of this engine were sent to the War Office for evaluation. Any intended development of the DFW biplane was brought to an abrupt halt when, late in 1914 following the outbreak of hostilities, the newly formed Ministry of Munitions, wishing to secure increased output, asked Beardmore to undertake the building of existing aircraft types. The

Company immediately drew up plans for the building of aircraft construction sheds at Dalmuir. Beardmore's DFW seaplane was subsequently pressed into service with the Royal Naval Air Service.

The speed with which the first aircraft orders arrived – for BE2c's – obliged the Company to start work in the shipyard Joiners Shop and it was not until the end of 1915 that the first phase of the Seaplane Sheds, as they were known, was completed. Despite that, the first aircraft were delivered on 8 March 1915. A total of 60 Be2c's were built. Early in 1915, encouraged by the Ministry, the Company established an aircraft design office to produce original aircraft designs for evaluation.[21] The necessary expertise to run such an office was provided by Lieutenant George Tilghman Richards who, in his capacity as an Aircraft Inspector, was already familiar with the Company. Richards resigned his commission and set about the creation of the small design team at Dalmuir.[22]

Under Richards, a series of aircraft were designed and a few prototypes built. The most successful of these developments was the WBIII described as '. . . one of the most imaginative (if

A naval rating and a woman worker at a bench vice by the fitting-out basin in 1918.

Sopwith Camels and WB V's at Robertson Park Dalmuir. Aircraft were wheeled from the Aviation Sheds to the small hangars at Robertson's Park where the wings were fitted.

one of the less successful) air undertakings on the British technical record'[23] This aircraft was based on the Sopwith Pup for which the company had received orders to build 80. The Pup was considerably modified to permit, among other things, better stowage on board aircraft-carrying ships and included the fitting of folding wings, flotation gear, jury struts, wingtip skids and in some, a retractable undercarriage. In later machines, the undercarriage was fixed but jettisonable to allow emergency alighting on water. Pup number 9950, the last aircraft from the first batch to be built at Dalmuir, was used as the prototype for succeeding WBIIIs. Orders for 100 aircraft of this type were received.

Thirty two Wight seaplanes, 50 Nieuport 12 fighters and a total of 140 Sopwith 2F.1 Camels were built at Dalmuir, the first flight of the latter taking place on 20 February 1918. A further 35 Camels were built by Arrol Johnston at Dumfries.

The largest aircraft built by Beardmore, the four engined Handley Page V/1500 bomber, was initially assembled in the airship shed and later in a purpose built aircraft shed beside the airship shed at Inchinnan. An initial order for twenty machines was received on 13 March 1918 followed by an order for a further thirty in July, although this order was cancelled in December. Production of the first batch stretched into 1919 and eleven of these were delivered as spare parts and not erected. A total of 487 aircraft and twelve kite balloons were made at Dalmuir during the war period in addition to repair and experimental work and the manufacture of various spares. Some indication of the efforts made by the firm can be seen through the following telegram sent to Dalmuir on 10 April 1918 from General Alexander, Aerosupply, London.

'The Secretary of State for Air and Air Council ask me to convey to your firm, your staff and your workers, their sincere thanks and appreciation of your able efforts during the past six months, which

The first Beardmore designed and built aircraft, the WBI was a two-seat bomber. The aircraft never went into production and this example is the only one built.

The WBIII fighter was based on the Sopwith Pup but was modified by Beardmore to make it more suitable for shipboard use. This particular example was the prototype.

have enabled the Royal Air Force in the field to receive such satisfactory supply of aircraft equipment, and to make good their losses so well, through the unexampled fighting of last month'[24]

THE SEAPLANE SHEDS

Phase One of the Seaplane Sheds was a building which comprised four bays each of which was 80 feet wide by 160 feet long. The two centre bays were used for aircraft assembly while the bays to either side housed joiners and mechanics shops.

Soon after completion, galleries were added to house fabric and wing shops. Frames, girders and other parts for airships were also manufactured in this area from 1915 onwards until new facilities were created at Inchinnan. The second phase was the building of drawing and administration offices to the west of the original sheds and later still, additional space in the form of a small bay was provided to the east of the main sheds where

fabric was 'doped' and aircraft parts were packed. These hangars were of typical construction for the period having gently arched corrugated iron roofs with glazed lights supported by timber 'Belfast' roof trusses.

Wheeled aircraft were taken to a strip of land close to the works known as Robertson's Park where a small grass airfield for flying-off Beardmore built aircraft was levelled. Two small hangars were erected here in 1916 where the wings were fitted to the fuselages. The aircraft were then flown to Renfrew or Inchinnan Aerodrome both of which were designated as Aircraft Acceptance Parks for locally built aircraft. Seaplanes were taken directly from the erection bays through large sliding doors at the river's edge where they were lowered into the Clyde by means of a small crane. By 1918 the Aviation Department at Dalmuir was large enough to build 15 small, 20 medium and 6 large aircraft simultaneously.[25]

The interior of the newly completed Aviation Sheds at Dalmuir showing a number of BE2c aircraft under construction in 1915. The sheds ran parallel to the Clyde which was only a few feet away.

AIRSHIPS

In contrast to the extensive development and building programme initiated by the Germans, British interest in rigid airships was half hearted and spasmodic in the years leading up to World War One. When this gave way to firm commitment, a similar situation existed with the construction of airships as it did with submarines in that Vickers was, once again, the only firm in the country with any experience. In characteristic pioneering style, Vickers had commenced construction of the first British rigid airship, the Mayfly, in 1909 which on completion in 1911, broke her back minutes after being taken out of her shed for only the second time. After this, serious interest in rigids waned until 1913 when several prominent figures within the Admiralty including Admiral John Jellicoe, then Second Sea Lord and in charge of the Naval Air Service, urged 'the building of a fleet of Zeppelins on behalf of the Navy'.[26] Debate on the relative merits of the airship over aircraft ensued, although it was generally agreed that in their present state of development, aircraft did not offer the extended radius of action required in fleet reconnaissance.

In April 1913, Vickers set up an Airship Department following an Admiralty request that they should produce designs for an experimental airship similar to the German Zeppelins. The order for an airship (designated No 9) was placed in June 1914 but doubts over the desirability of completing this airship, which led to a stoppage of all work on 12 March 1915 for a period of three months, delayed completion until April 1917. In the summer of 1915, it was decided that work should proceed on no fewer than four airships – including No 9 – for use in the fleet reconnaissance role.

With no established builders other than Vickers, the Admiralty 'invited' both Beardmore and Armstrong Whitworth to participate in the airship programme. The necessary finance to build airship constructional hangars was provided, much to the chagrin of Vickers who had spent considerable sums in creating their own facilities. For Beardmore, this was not the first interest

The vast Airship Shed at Inchinnan, built by Arrol in considerable secrecy, was 720 feet long, 230 feet wide and 122 feet high. This impressive structure was completed in less than nine months. The cottage to the left was demolished on completion of the shed.

The girders for airship No. 24 were manufactured at Dalmuir and brought over to Inchinnan for erection in the Airship Shed. This airship was left in the open for six months as a test for mooring techniques.

expressed in airships as in late 1913 application for airship patents had been made although no further action had taken place.

On 16 October, the first order was placed for three airships of the 23 Class – expansions of Vickers' No 9 design. Beardmore's order was for airship No 24 and the manufacture of parts was immediately started in the recently completed first phase of the Seaplane Sheds at Dalmuir. The remaining orders were given, one each, to Vickers (No 23) and Armstrong (No 25).

Limited space at Dalmuir precluded erection of the 535 foot long airship there and a suitably flat expanse of land was sought as close to the shipyard as possible where new works could be laid out. In the interim, the facilities at Dalmuir were used to the full and all the parts for the Company's first two and much of the third airship orders were manufactured there. Land for the new works was found about 1.5 miles south of the yard on the other side of the Clyde at Inchinnan, which comprised little more than a few cottages, farms and a church. Under the Defence of the Realm Regulations, a total of 413 acres of land were taken over for the building of the Airship Constructional Station in which Beardmore's role was constructor under Admiralty supervision. Ground was also acquired at Inchinnan for an aerodrome and Aircraft Acceptance Park.[27] To enable the erection of airship No 24 to proceed at

the earliest moment possible, plans were quickly drawn up for the construction of a spectacularly large airship shed, the contract for which was given to Sir William Arrol.

Work began on the construction of this shed on 5 January 1916 and was completed on 30 September of the same year. However, by 21 July the shed was advanced enough to permit the laying down of the first frames of No 24 which had been transported across the river from Dalmuir. The remarkably quick construction of the airship shed, which must have been one of the largest structures in the country, is a fitting tribute to the ability and expertise of the Arrol Company. Two other Constructional Stations were built at the same time – Armstrong Whitworth's near Selby and Shorts at Cardington.

The country setting of the Inchinnan Works posed severe problems for the new airship workers many of whom were driven to the site each morning by charabanc from Renfrew. In consideration of this, the Company pressed on with the building of 52 houses for key workers located a discret half mile away from the works. This development known then as now as 'Beardmore Cottages' was described in the following manner in the March 1919 edition of *Beardmore News* – 'A village has been erected near the Inchinnan Works for the accommodation of a number of the workers and this village is looked upon as a model as it gives to

the working man all the comfort and convenience of self contained houses, and that at very moderate rents'. The houses were attractive and comfortable and compared more than favourably with the shipyard worker's tenements then under construction at Dalmuir, although this is perhaps less due to the status of airship workers – mostly drawn from the shipyard anyway – than to the small number of houses required.

A complete airship works was built at Inchinnan over the next two years and on completion comprised the following manufacturing areas —

Airship Shed
Frame Shop
Girder Shop
Car Shop
Fabric Shop
Gasbag Testing Shop
Silicol Plant House (Hydrogen Plant)
Gasholders
Bottle Storage Area
Boiler House for Anti Freezing Plant
Electric Power Station[28]

There were also numerous small stores for petrol, paraffin and paint etc. and a meteorological hut. Quarters and messes for officers and men were located away from the works on the other side of the main Greenock – Glasgow Road. The airship shed, shops and buildings occupied an area of 31 acres.[29] Plans were also on hand to construct a second airship shed parallel to the first although this development did not take place. A further proposal to erect a large Aircraft Acceptance Shed to receive aircraft built in factories throughout the Glasgow area did not proceed either. However a large hangar known as the Handley Page shed was built for the construction and erection of Handley Page V/1500 four engined bombers.

THE AIRSHIP SHED

The exterior dimensions of this massive shed, which was almost as impressive as the airships themselves, were 720 feet long, 230 feet wide on the ground and 122 feet high to the roof ridges. Internally there was a clear space of 720 feet by 153 feet wide and 100 feet to the underside of the roof girders – easily enough to permit erection of two Class 23 airships side by side. The extra width at the base of the shed was used to form what were termed the 'annexes' – areas given over to stores, workshops and offices.

A series of 'panic doors' were fitted to either side of the shed in the event that rapid departure should prove desirable. A full time fire officer was appointed whose duty was to prevent fires breaking out rather than deal with them when they had. To achieve a night-time blackout, all windows, which were glazed with tinted glass, were fitted with

R27 first flew in June 1918. Her 18 gas bags contained 990,000 cubic feet of hydrogen. After logging 90 hours of flight, she was burnt-out in her shed at Howden in August 1918.

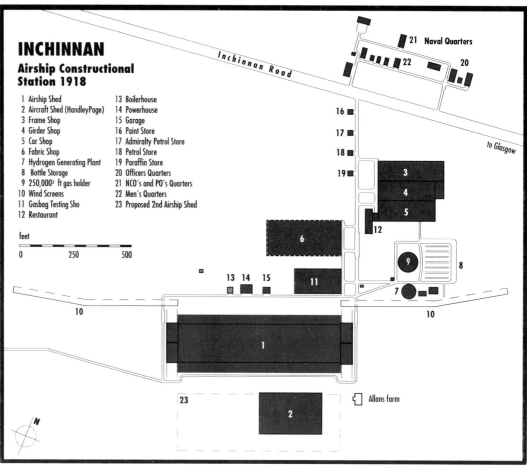

INCHINNAN
**Airship Constructional
Station 1918**

1 Airship Shed
2 Aircraft Shed (HandleyPage)
3 Frame Shop
4 Girder Shop
5 Car Shop
6 Fabric Shop
7 Hydrogen Generating Plant
8 Bottle Storage
9 250,000³ ft gas holder
10 Wind Screens
11 Gasbag Testing Sho
12 Restaurant
13 Boilerhouse
14 Powerhouse
15 Garage
16 Paint Store
17 Admiralty Petrol Store
18 Petrol Store
19 Paraffin Store
20 Officers Quarters
21 NCO's and PO's Quarters
22 Men's Quarters
23 Proposed 2nd Airship Shed

feet
0   250   500

blinds which could be operated from a few centrally located points. The columns facing into the erection bay were fitted with canvas pads to prevent chaffing against the sides of the airships once they had become buoyant. The shed was steel framed and clad in galvanised steel sheet. There were two massive sliding doors at both ends of the shed each counterbalanced with several hundred tons of concrete to prevent blowing over when opened. These doors were opened manually by means of a capstan which was fitted on a platform at the bottom of the door. An estimated 13 minutes was required for a team of men to open each door by turning the capstan. A 700 foot long, 60 foot high sheet steel wind-break was built at either end of the Airship Shed to prevent the airships being buffeted on removal from the shed.[30]

THE AIRSHIPS

Airship No 24 of the 23 Class made her maiden flight from Inchinnan without mishap on 21 July 1917. The next airship type to be built was the

23X Class, a version of the 23 Class with improved endurance and an internal keel. Beardmore was initially awarded the contract to build Nos 27 and 28 of this class. No 27 was laid down on 16 March 1917 and first flew on 8 April 1918. Material for No 28 was in hand at Dalmuir when it was decided to move the contract to Vickers and finally, to cancel her outright in August 1917.

The next airship design to be built was the 33 Class based closely on the German L30 Class an example of which, the L33, had been brought down almost intact on the Essex coast in September 1916. These craft were found to be so superior to the British types that the design was copied. Of this new class, the R34 was given to Beardmore and she was laid down at Inchinnan on 9 December 1917. The 33 Class was considerably larger than previous classes with a total volume of nearly 2 million cubic feet and overall dimensions of 643 feet by 75 feet. The R34 first flew on 20 December 1918 and made history in July of the following year when she became the first aircraft to fly the Atlantic in both directions.

Above. The R34 over Inchinnan. In July 1919 the R34 became the first aircraft to make the double journey across the Atlantic ocean. The newly completed 'Handley Page Shed' is to the right of the airship shed.

Left. Inside the shed at Inchinnan where the R34 is under construction.

On completion of this voyage, the Admiralty sent the following telegram to the Company; 'Hearty congratulations on the splendid performance of the R34, to the success of which the good workmanship and cordial co-operation of your firm have so greatly contributed'.[31]

Like most other airships, the R34 had an exceedingly short life. In January 1921 at Howden Airship Station, she received substantial damage to her forward section after being moored out in a gale and had to be scrapped. Had Howden been equipped with a mooring mast, prototypes of which were then under development, the airship would have been able to ride out the storm.

On 5 January 1917, three further airships, based this time on a study of the captured German Zeppelin L48, were ordered. Of this class, known as the R35 Class, the R36 was given to Beardmore and she was laid down following the completion and departure of the R34. Shortly after the Armistice, work on R36 was suspended while

fresh consideration could be given to her future deployment.

ARTILLERY

Following the start of the war in August 1914, the demand for artillery and shells was immediate. As was the case with warship building, the Government naturally turned to those companies, in addition to the Royal Ordnance Factories, who were already experienced in the manufacture of artillery. The Beardmore Company had little involvement in this facet of the armaments industry and it was only after September 1914, when the demand for heavy field artillery became pressing, that the Company was asked to commence production. At Dalmuir, new shops were built in five phases the first of which was begun in November 1914, the others, which took the form of extensions to the first, had all been started by October 1915. On completion, the Field Carriage Shops covered an area of seven

The first Beardmore built Handley Page V/1500 four engined bomber E-8287 at Inchinnan in 1919. The aircraft is standing in front of one of the two camouflaged 60 foot high windscreens which were at either end of the airship shed to prevent cross winds buffeting airships.

acres and cost approximately £62,000 which was provided by the Government. The plant specialised in the production of 6 inch howitzers and 18 pounder field gun carriages but also produced one hundred 2 pounder gun mountings, four triple 4 inch gun mountings destined for the large cruisers of the Courageous class and a large quantity of Leon mines. The Parkhead works supplied the barrels and breach mechanisms

In 1915, a fuse loading works was built at the eastern end of the works on vacant ground, with additional ground available for extensions should this be necessary. These works, which were not extensive and consisted mostly of earthworks and covered passageways, were moved in 1917 to new premises at Anniesland in Glasgow. A small shop for the building of tanks was also erected to the west of the fitting-out basin but after fifty Mark IV tanks had been constructed, production ceased as the pressure of warship orders particularly destroyers and submarines, required the urgent return of the riveters to shipbuilding work.

WARTIME EXTENSIONS

Throughout the war period, Naval Construction Works at Dalmuir were under continual expansion. In addition to the covered submarine berths and associated shops of the new West Yard, the new aviation, artillery and tank shops, the capacity of the main shipyard itself was increased significantly. In 1918, major extensions to the platers shed and mechanics shops were opened provided almost the same floor area again as the original shops. Numerous smaller additions included a new brass foundry, pipe shop and a torpedo shop which appears to have been exclusively involved with the production of mines.

What had started off in 1906 as a shipyard and engine works, had by 1918, become a manufacturing centre for a remarkable and varied range of armaments which were organised into the following departments;

A V1500 and a Sopwith Pup in front of the airship shed at Inchinnan in 1919. The R36 is under construction in the shed.

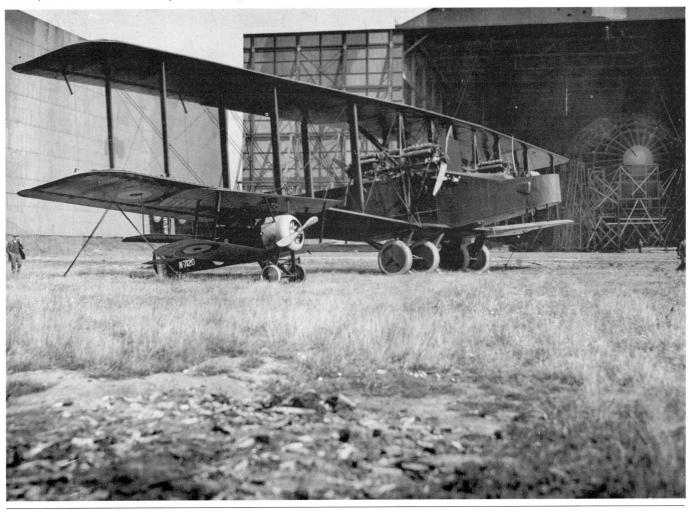

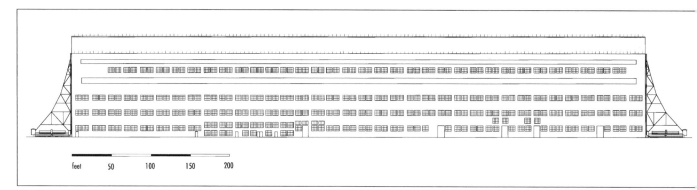

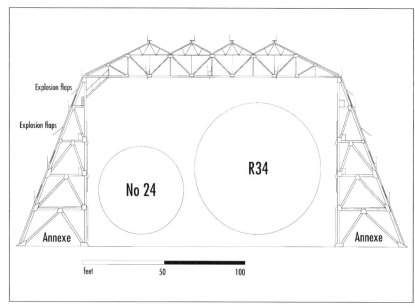

Top. South elevation of the airship shed at Inchinnan.

Above. A section through the shed showing the extreme diameters of No 24 and R36. This drawing and the one above are based on original Arrol drawings.

SHIPBUILDING DEPARTMENT.
Main Yard 6 berths.
West Yard (Submarine Sheds) 4 Berths
Vessels of all types.

ENGINE AND BOILER DEPARTMENT.
Turbine and reciprocating machinery together with boilers for ships built in the yard plus additional engines, including semi-diesels, and boilers for vessels building elsewhere.

AVIATION DEPARTMENT.
Seaplanes, single seat fighters, four engined bombers, rigid and non-rigid airships. (Inchinnan Works managed from Dalmuir)

ARTILLERY DEPARTMENT.
6 inch howitzers, 8 inch howitzers, 18 pounder field guns, 2 pounder field guns, 4 inch naval mountings, Leon mines.

FUSE DEPARTMENT.
(Quantity produced unknown.)

TANK DEPARTMENT.
(50 Mark IV tanks built)

ACCOMMODATION

In 1915, 16,000 workers travelled daily from Glasgow to the shipyards in Dalmuir and Clydebank and once more the problem of accommodation in the district became acute.[32] In response to this, the Beardmore Company formed the Dalmuir and West of Scotland Estates Company Ltd, in 1915, charged with the task of building and managing new tenements for workers. As early as 1901 William Beardmore had personally purchased 5.85 acres of land from the Dunn-Pattison Estate for the sum of £4,437, 8, 6d. On this land, it had been intended to build workers' tenements shortly after the first phase of tenement building which had taken place in 1906/07. This proved to be unnecessary as the disappointing performance of the shipyard had attracted significantly fewer workers than initially envisaged. This land was now sold to the Estates Company by William Beardmore for the original purchase price and work commenced on the building of tenements. The first scheme, for 33 tenements, was ready for occupation by October 1916; the second, for 18 tenements, by March 1917. The 51 tenements and new roads so far constructed cost £92,500. Work proceeded slowly on an additional 20 tenements which were not completed until late 1920. A total of seventy one new tenements were built together with six new roads.[33] The roads were given names commemorating fleet and field commanders – Jellicoe Street, Beatty Street, French Street, Kitchener Street and so on. The tenements were built with flat roofs, because of wartime shortages which precluded the construction of the more elaborate traditional pitched roof. Lead for plumbing purposes was not available, and initially, iron pipes were ordered until lead was obtainable again at the end of the war.

To provide more immediate accommodation,

Left. The only WBIV single-seat torpedo plane built shown here in Robertson's Park Dalmuir in 1917.

Below. A 6-inch howitzer photographed outside the general office at Dalmuir.

8-inch Mark VII Howitzers in the Field Carriage shops.

Below. A 6-inch naval gun on a pedestal mounting fitted with Beardmore rim grip friction training gear.

Left. Eight 4-inch naval mountings. The caption under the original photograph stated this was one week's output.

Below. An 18-pounder Mark III field gun.

Above. A series of Mark V tanks under construction in erecting shops still to be completed.

Right. A 4-inch Mark 1 triple naval mounting of the type fitted to battlecruisers of the period.

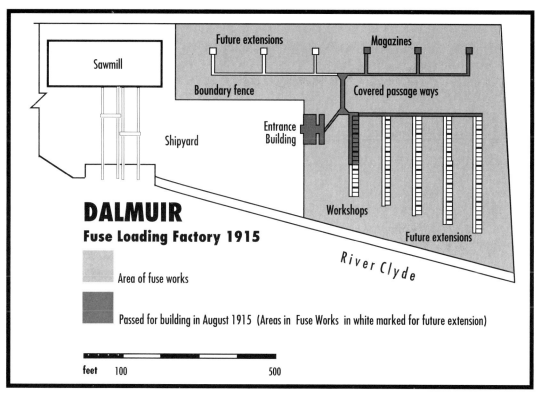

Sawmill

Future extensions

Magazines

Boundary fence

Covered passage ways

Shipyard

Entrance
Building

DALMUIR
Fuse Loading Factory 1915

Workshops

Future extensions

River Clyde

Area of fuse works

Passed for building in August 1915 (Areas in Fuse Works in white marked for future extension)

feet   100   500

*Left. The Fuse Loading
Factory as built at the east
end of the yard in 1916.
Earth was piled high around
each magazine to minimise
the effect of blast should an
accident occur. The works
were relocated at Anniesland
before the war ended.*

*Below. Six 6-inch howitzers
arranged in the packing shed
after the end of the war.*

the Company undertook the construction of a workmans' 'Hotel' named the Benbow Hotel, in Agamemnon Street adjacent to the yard. The four storey Benbow Hotel was opened in May 1916 and contained 386 bedrooms on the top three floors. Each floor was served by four bathrooms (each containing two baths) and numerous lavatories. Each bedroom, which measured only 7' 6" by 5' 4", had a window, and was fitted with an electric light, wardrobe, mirror, chair and a folding bed. On the ground floor there were separate dining saloons, a public one for one thousand persons, another reserved for draughtsmen foremen and women workers and a third for residents. Special features of the Hotel included a hairdressers, a laundry and billiard, recreation, writing and reading rooms reflecting Beardmore's concern for the welfare of his workers.[14]

Following previous unfavourable experiences of similar developments in the district, the people of Dalmuir were doubtless gratified to be told by A J Campbell at the opening, that the Benbow Hotel was, 'No howf for weary Willies but a place where good clean comfortable, airy and homely lodgings would be provided for honest working men'. This building was bombed and totally destroyed during the Clydebank Blitz in 1941.

According to the valuation role, by 1920, the Company owned directly or indirectly, through the Estates Company, 149 tenement buildings. Most of these buildings housed an average of eleven separate apartments, giving an approximate total in excess of 1,600 workers' flats.

During the war other difficulties, well chronicled elsewhere, had a bearing on the shipyard although they were not peculiar to the Dalmuir district; the Rents Strike of 1915 and the introduction of dilution to the works during 1916. Workers' housing was stretched to the limit during the war period as a result of the great influx of additional labour into the machine shops and shipyards. Perhaps taking advantage of this, landlords put rents up and in doing so inflamed an already difficult position for many people who had also to contend with price rises in basic foodstuffs as well as their kin answering Lord Kitchener's challenge to join the colours. Inability to pay the new rents resulted in evictions which, in turn, prompted the 'Rents Strike' of 1915 in Glasgow. Dalmuir shipyard workers became involved directly as evicted persons and indirectly in a strike throughout the Glasgow area which added weight to the wave of protest. When finally the Government intervened, rents were frozen at the 1913 level until 1920.

To ease the acute shortage of housing during the war the company built more tenements at Dalmuir. Wartime shortages of building material resulted in these tenements being completed with flat roofs. This photograph, of Dumbarton Road taken in 1968, shows Beardmore flat-roofed tenements facing their more traditional counterparts.

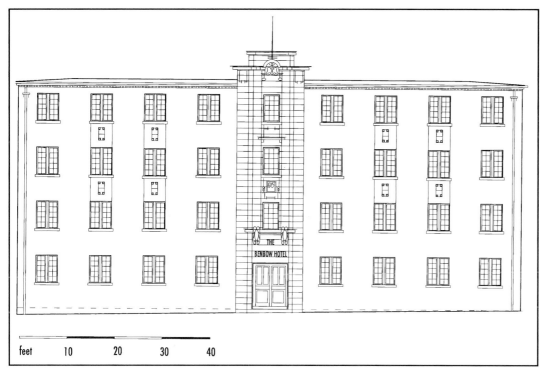

The main elevation of The Benbow Hotel as seen from Agamemnon Street.

The issue of dilution was equally grievous until it was resolved during the spring of 1916 and, although the leadership of the fight against dilution had its base at Beardmore's Parkhead works, Dalmuir was nevertheless in full support of the action taken by the parent works and elsewhere on the Clyde. The nearest the Dalmuir works got to any form of political organisation was in the form of an *ad hoc* 'economic class' of no more than a dozen men who met to discus Marxism behind the Submarine Sheds at lunch time.[35]

On the declaration of war in 1914, 500 men left the shipyard to join the armed forces. Ultimately a total of 1,625 men joined-up and of these, 181 were killed. On 29 August 1914 a War Relief Fund was set up and when this fund was closed in July 1919, a total of £48,645 had been collected. This money was disbursed weekly to 954 wives and widowed mothers on whom 1618 persons were dependent.[36] A war memorial bearing the names of the dead was unveiled at the works entrance on 6 May 1921. This memorial is now in Dalmuir Park.

Below. Departmental stamps taken from surviving documents

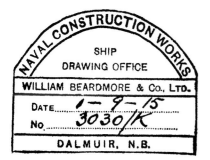

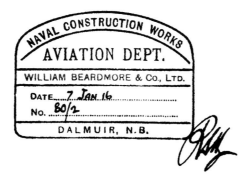

Post War Boom and After: 1919 – 1923

Not surprisingly, the end of the War brought a rapid halt to the ordering of all war materials. Initially this brought few problems for the armaments firms, who, forewarned of the need to consider this eventuality by the Government in early 1918, prepared to enter into what was expected to be a sustained period of growth in shipbuilding to reinstate the depleted merchant fleets of the world. Various other interesting manufacturing opportunities were emerging, made possible by the advances in wartime technology, such as commercial airships and aircraft. It was with precisely these developments, as well as with road and rail transport, that Sir William hoped to concentrate and direct his Company. In 1919, he put it this way;

> 'It was as though in 1914 when the war commenced, we had to create nationally a huge wheel. We had to set it in motion, gradually getting up the speed for a considerable time, and by this huge store of energy overcome the munitions shortage. Since the Armistice, we have had to take the energy out of the wheel and slowly and gradually reverse its direction of motion. That you will agree is no easy thing to do – to reverse a wheel of such gigantic proportions as we were running during the war. We now have a big task in front of us, and I think history will relegate to us for the manner in which we have reversed this wheel and turned it into peace products'.[1]

The only prospect for naval orders on a scale resembling the years leading up to the War, lay in the knowledge that the American and Japanese Governments had embarked upon massive building programmes for large and powerful ships – in effect, a new naval race from which Britain could not remain detached for long.

However, at Dalmuir shipyard, several ships left over from the Emergency War Programmes lay on the stocks while the Admiralty decided their fate. At the launch of the cruiser *Raleigh* on 28th August 1919, Sir William Beardmore referred to instructions received earlier that week from the First Lord of the Admiralty, Eric Long, to cancel the destroyer *Vimy*, the submarine *L70* and the airship *R40*. Sir William hoped that the *Raleigh* 'would survive the pruning hand which had been applied so liberally to warship production'. He added that employment at Dalmuir in light of these cancellations would not be affected as there was plenty of merchant work available.[2] Ironically, the *Raleigh* was launched by the First Lord's wife, Lady Long.

Two sloops, the *Clive* and *Lawrence* which were to have been laid-down before the outbreak of war, were finally laid-down in late 1918.

The first major merchant order, for two passenger ships, came from the Glasgow based Anchor Line These vessels, *Cameronia* and *Tyrrhenia*, were laid down in early 1919 and were followed about six months later by two Italian liners, the *Conte Rosso* and the *Conte Verde* for the Lloyd Sabaudo Line of Genoa whose original order for the *Conte Rosso* in 1914 had been

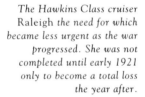

The Hawkins Class cruiser Raleigh *the need for which became less urgent as the war progressed. She was not completed until early 1921 only to become a total loss the year after.*

transformed into the aircraft carrier *Argus*. In mid 1920, two large passenger cargo vessels, *Esperance Bay* and *Largs Bay*, were laid down for the Commonwealth Government Line of Australia as part of a five ship order, the other three of which went to Vickers at Barrow. The *Setter*, a small ferry for Glasgow owners G and J Burns, and intended for the Glasgow Belfast service was also ordered. By the beginning of 1920, the shipyard had on order no fewer than ten ships including the *Raleigh*, the majority of which were, by the standard of the day, large and well appointed.

No doubt this apparent abundance of orders did much to confirm Sir William Beardmore, and other shipbuilders alike, in their belief of a sustained boom in shipbuilding. To take advantage of this, Beardmore decided in early 1920, to extend his shipyard at the earliest possible time by laying out four new berths at the eastern end of the yard on the site of the former fuse works which were now to be removed. Optimistically, Beardmore intended that large warships and passenger vessels would continue to be built at the main yard, while smaller cargo ships and oil tankers would be constructed in the new East Yard where it was hoped that this could be carried out more economically. This yard would almost certainly have been built during the war had permission from the Admiralty been forthcoming.[3]

THE EAST YARD

To provide additional space for this development, the narrow strip of land separating Beardmore's yard from John Brown's was purchased from the latter for the sum of £2,500.[4] Work began on the yard in mid March 1920 when Arrol's commenced construction of a coffer dam at the water's edge to enable the declivity of the ways to be formed and piling to start. On completion a year later, the East Yard comprised four berths two of which were 500 feet long, one 550 feet long and the other 450 feet long. All were 70 feet wide. The berths were served by four fixed 'Toplis' luffing cranes made by Stothert & Pitt of Bath. These cranes were acquired from the Disposal Board in London whose tasks included the selling-off of equipment installed in the National Shipyards which had been set-up at Chepstow to boost the wartime output of merchant ships. These were the first luffing jib cranes to be used for shipbuilding on the river Clyde. They had a lift of five tons at 110 feet and were considered to be the equivalent

of eighteen derricks and eight steam winches.

As the new East Yard was located some distance from the main platers shed and other departments, a new platers shed, electric power station, compressor house general store and time office were built along with a new works entrance. On launching, vessels were to be taken to the existing fitting-out basin for completion. The new platers shed was 300 feet long by 150 feet wide and was divided into three equal bays each of which was served by an overhead travelling crane of five tons capacity. Plates were carried to this shed from the main stockyard by a ten ton capacity travelling steam crane. Overall, the East Yard covered twelve

The Allan liner Alsatian still wearing disruptive camouflage after service as an armed merchant cruiser, returns to Dalmuir for a refit.

The Toplis crane built by Stothert & Pitt. Beardmore introduced the luffing crane for shipbuilding purposes to the river Clyde.

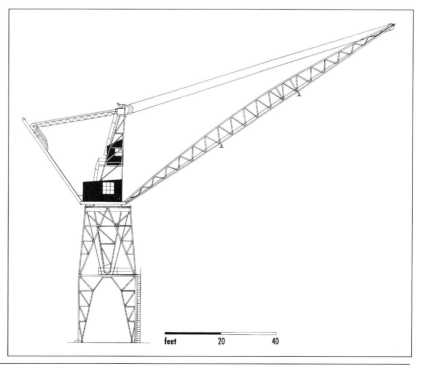

feet   20   40

acres and with the additional land purchased from Brown's, placed the total area of Dalmuir shipyard at over one hundred acres with a river frontage of 1.25 miles – easily the biggest yard on the Clyde. A figure of £260,000 is recorded against the four berths in the new East Yard.[5]

At this time Dalmuir shipyard was credited with an annual capacity of 100,000 tons compared to 90,000 tons for John Brown and 48,000 tons for Fairfield. The first ship to be launched out of the new East Yard was the appropriately named *British Enterprise* on 18 October 1921 for the British Tanker Company. This was part of a two ship order which was subsequently increased to five. *British Trader* was laid down at the main yard, while the remaining three, *British Commerce, British Industry* and *British Merchant*, took up the remaining three berths at the new East Yard.

The creation of this new shipyard viewed against the demand for ships in 1919 and early 1920, together with a widely held belief in a prolonged period of growth, was sound enough. Unfortunately however, Sir William Beardmore's characteristically rapid response to market conditions was not rewarded. By the end of 1920

when the new yard was all but complete, the demand for new tonnage had dropped sharply as shipping rates fell and the world moved slowly into the depressed years of the 1920s. With no surviving Company records to confirm, it seems likely that no more than a handful of ships were built in this yard. Beardmore was not the only one caught in this expensive trap. Upriver, the Fairfield shipyard laid out four new berths the completion of which coincided with the start of the depression.[6]

WELFARE DEPARTMENT

In late 1918, the Company, in common with other firms at this time, established a Welfare Department primarily to assist management in 'keeping in touch' with the young persons in their employment. Instruction was given to apprentices on a variety of topics and in view of the increasing specialisation of shop work, an attempt was made to give apprentices and other young workers an insight into the range of skills and occupations in the shipyard upon which their own work would finally depend. The Welfare Department also succeeded in improving time keeping and sought to enlist parents' help in the supervision of young

The Beardmore Welfare Swimming Club.

workers. When the order-book was low and employment affected, every effort was made to maintain continuity of employment for apprentices and to save their career from a break at an age when even temporary illness might be fatal to both mental and moral welfare. As a consequence of this attitude, apprentices were switched from one department to another during difficult times or, if need be, arrangements were made for their transfer to another works altogether.[7]

Shortly after the inception of the Welfare Department, a Welfare Supervisor was appointed. This was a gentleman by the name of H Walker Arnott who took up this appointment on being demobilised from the Royal Scots Fusiliers and who insisted that apprentices address him as Captain Arnott.

Schemes were implemented to encourage apprentices to attend evening classes to give greater depth and understanding to the training received in the shipyard. Incentive was provided in the form of a cash bonus paid weekly, the size of which was determined by the level of success achieved in examinations. Thus a first-year apprentice scoring a pass rate of 70% was entitled to receive an extra six pence per week. 80% qualified for nine pence per week while a score of 90% earned one shilling. The money value was increased with each year of the apprenticeship and it was possible for an apprentice to supplement his wages by as much as 10%. Alternatively, this weekly bonus could be saved by the Welfare Department and paid out as a lump sum prior to the annual summer holiday.

The passing of the Education (Scotland) Act in 1918, had several ramifications for employers. The school leaving age was increased to fifteen and attendance of all young employed persons at

The erecting shop in the recently converted locomotive works during 1922. In the foreground is Prince of Wales class 4-6-0 locomotive works no 259 under construction.

'day continuation' classes was made compulsory for a period of three years with a minimum of 320 hours to be provided for education each year. The new proposals were considered to be more desirable than the voluntary evening classes then offered to young persons and, in addition to training in the craft of their choice, the new scheme provided young apprentices with an element of general education so that the wider interests of education were served. In general, the aims of the new act were to better equip young persons for not just earning a living but also to prepare them for social life and leisure. Sir William chose to provide the facilities for this programme of day education within his establishment at Dalmuir. The old school buildings adjacent to the works' main entrance and redundant in a civic sense since the

opening of a larger school elsewhere, had been bought by Beardmore when the shipyard was first laid out and it was appropriately enough in this building that the new school opened. Additional facilities within the school provided for its use as a club, committee rooms and a gymnasium. On the 23 January 1920, Sir William opened the school with classes for the following departments within the works; Engineering, Locomotive, Shipbuilding, Boilermaking, Woodworking and General Office.

In the early 1920s, the purchase of working tools and clothing by apprentices was made easier by the weekly deduction from their wages of a small sum over a period of time. The basic items involved included a khaki shirt at 2/6d, a boiler suit at 7/6d and a pair of boots at 15/- for which

The locomotive repair bay in the main engine and boiler shops (No 3 bay) during 1920. At least twelve 0-6-0T locomotives are under repair in the foreground with many other types beyond. A destroyer funnel can be seen to the extreme left of shot.

anything from one shilling upwards could be made in weekly repayments. Apprentice joiners, carpenters and patternmakers were supplied with sufficient tools to enable them to start work, repayment of one shilling per week usually being completed in a little over one year. To complement the instructional and other work undertaken by the Welfare Department, recreational activities were started and developed during the early 1920s. The old school was the venue for most of these activities.

Beardmore Naval Cadets, drawn from works apprentices, were inaugurated under the instruction of Captain Arnott with classes taken in seamanship, knots and splices, signalling and later, the wireless. On 28 February 1920, 150 Beardmore Cadets were inspected at Dalmuir by Captain Thesiger from the Admiralty who was visiting similar groups of cadets elsewhere in the country. His report noted that this was the largest unit he had inspected and added that . . . 'I heard with great pleasure that generally speaking, the Cadets of the Corps, did not smoke to the extent that is common amongst other boys in Scotland.'[8]

Once formed, the Wireless Section had the use of a three valve set and one lecture in March 1923 on the theme of 'wireless listening-in' was given – according to *Beardmore News* – to a capacity audience. The Naval Cadets had three boats, two twenty-four foot long cutters and a larger one called *Elma* which had previously been owned by the Irish nationalist campaigner and author Erskine Childers. A summer camp was run for the cadets at Meigle in Perthshire.

Other works' clubs were founded including football, boxing, weight-lifting, badminton, gymnastics, a harriers' section and photography. This understandable desire to develop new interests and activities in the early 1920s led to some rather unusual combinations in the name of sport – and so it was that a ladies team took to the hockey field and roundly thrashed the men of the Aircraft Designing Office in March 1920. The score was not recorded. An Aviation Engineering Society was formed in March 1925 with membership standing at 109 while devotees of more cultural pursuits were accommodated by the formation, in late 1918, of the Beardmore (Dalmuir) Operatic Society. This had been prompted by the Ladies Welfare Supervisor, Mrs Reeves, who had pointed out that Dalmuir had no musical institution. In 1919, the Operatic Society

was able to perform the first in a series of annual presentations from the works of Gilbert and Sullivan. The *Mikado* was followed by the *Gondoliers*, the *Yeoman of the Guard* and the *Pirates of Penzance*. These productions usually ran for four nights at Clydebank Town Hall and were well supported by Sir William who was always in attendance with some of his works managers.

To raise funds for the 1923 presentation of *Princess Ida*, a Cake and Candy Sale was organised by the Society one Saturday afternoon and opened by A J Campbell's wife. Refreshments were provided 'at reasonable cost' together with a concert and various side shows such as billiards, table-tennis, quoits, pitch and putt, shooting and, of course, a demonstration by the Wireless Section. Subsequently, a note in the April 1923 edition of *Beardmore News* recorded that the Cake and Candy Sale had been a brilliant success even although only £80 had been raised instead of the hoped for £100.

LOCOMOTIVES

The end of the war had brought almost immediate redundancy to many of the shops erected and equipped specifically for the manufacture of field guns and Howitzers. In common with other armaments companies, Beardmore proposed to use these wartime extensions for the building of locomotives the manufacture of which was a logical extension of existing activities. This was also very much in accord with Sir William's view that the peace time activities of his Company should be even more closely identified with transportation on land, sea and air. The railways had been driven hard during the war years and, in addition to new construction, there was considerable back-log of locomotive repair work to be carried out.

At Dalmuir, the gun-mounting and Howitzer shops were completing the last wartime orders for 400 sets of eighteen pounder field guns. In the unlikely event that further orders for these weapons should be received, capacity for their construction was nevertheless maintained at the Parkhead Works, leaving the Dalmuir shops free for conversion to locomotive shops. The buildings were purchased by the Company from the Ministry of Munitions in 1920. Conversion necessitated a considerable amount of alteration to the structure of the buildings, none of which had been designed to cope with the much heavier loads associated with locomotive work. To support new overhead

Above. One of nineteen locomotives built in 1920 for Nigerian Railways. This is No 282 photographed on 13 November.

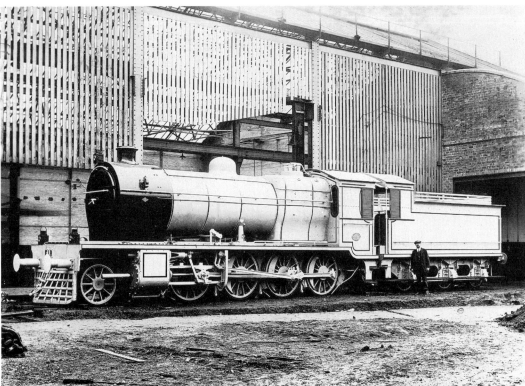

Right. Beardmore's first locomotive order was for thirty five 2-8-0s built for East Indian Railways. There is no number on the plate to identify whether or not this is the first Beardmore built locomotive.

cranes of up to 60 tons lift in some bays, girders bearing the crane rails had to be replaced with stronger ones. Walls were stiffened to support heavier loads. Much of the plant recently installed to manufacture field guns was stripped out and replaced with locomotive plant. The alterations were carried out simultaneously with the completion of the last field gun orders and great attention was paid to achieving a smooth transition from the old work to the new to avoid laying off employees.

On completion in the summer of 1920, the manufacturing sequence in the Locomotive Shops was as follows: Orders were progressed through the works in a west to east flow beginning at a new plate and bar stockyard; material from this stockyard was lifted by overhead crane as required and placed onto the works railway network for delivery to the appropriate shops. The main part of the works, all under one roof, was adjacent to the stockyard and ran in the following sequence; wheel and axle shop, cylinder shop, angle ironsmiths, tender, cab and splasher shop, inspection shop, machine shop, finishing shop, frame shop, tender erecting shop and finally the main locomotive erecting shop. To the north of these shops were smaller bays housing the tool room, copper shop, brass shop and smithy. [9]

To complete the works, several new sheds were constructed, including the steaming shed to the immediate south of the main erection bays. This shed contained a set of friction rolls for running tests. There was also a specially equipped packing shed where locomotives were dismantled and crated for dispatch, a rough material store and a hydraulic pumping station. Once crated for transit, the locomotives were taken the short distance to the fitting-out basin where the large 150 ton hammerhead crane lifted them aboard ship. Alternatively, locomotives could be run directly onto the main-line network which connected with the works own system. More

Left. Lady Invernairn steps down from an East Indian Railways locomotive during a visit to the yard on the occasion of the launch of the Tyrrhenia for the Cunard Line in May 1920.

A Prince of Wales class 4-6-0 No 258 in front of the general office at Dalmuir in April 1922. This locomotive was one of a batch of ninety ordered by the London & North Western Railway.

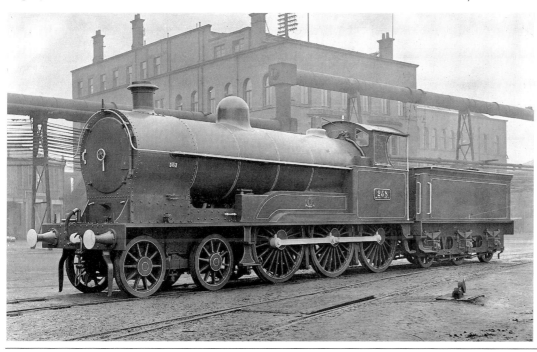

Six LNWR Prince of Wales 4-6-0s on a siding behind the works. The first locomotive is no 135, Beardmore works no. 178 built in August 1921. The locomotives have no coupling rods, chimneys or dome covers and are probably waiting to be hauled by rail for delivery to LNWR.

often, locomotives for export were shipped in running order a feature the Company made something of in advertisements of the period. Typical was the advert in *The Locomotive* of 15 October 1925 which stated that 25 locomotives for the Bombay Baroda & Central India Railway were loaded on board ship in 14.5 hours thereby eliminating all the costs associated with dismantling, checking, packing, rail to dock, unpacking, reassembling and testing.

A repair department was also established at Dalmuir, this being housed in No3 bay of the Engine and Boiler Shops. A large number of

Ministry of Supply 0-6-0 tank locomotives were repaired at Dalmuir during the early 1920s. The Parkhead works were also equipped with repair and boiler departments although all new construction was carried out at Dalmuir.

In August 1920 there was the prospect of Dalmuir, in conjunction with the Vickers works, sharing a huge order of 500 locomotives for the Rumanian State Railways, but this did not materialise. Other orders, if smaller, were taken however, the first being for 35 locomotives for the East Indian Railways, 20 for the Great Eastern Railway and 19 for Nigerian Railways. These

Simple line drawings of three Beardmore aircraft designed after the Great War but which were never built. Left is the large WBVIII, a 24 seat passenger triplane with separate passenger nacelles and line shafting to drive three propellers. In the middle is the WBVIA, a six passenger biplane. Right is the WBVI, a single-seat torpedo bomber. All three aircraft had folding wings.

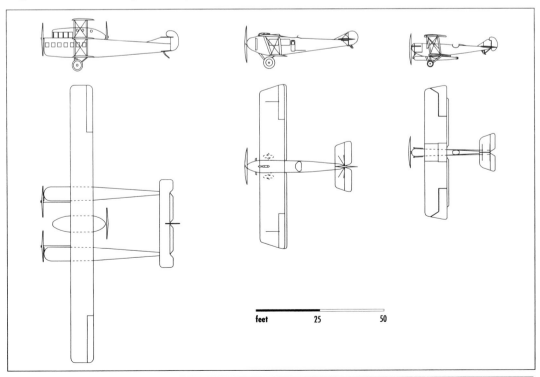

feet   25   50

orders were followed in 1920/21 by 90 locomotives for the London and North Western Railway.

AVIATION 1919 – 1924

When the end of the war brought a stop to the construction of aircraft throughout the country, most of the engineering concerns under Government sub-contract, ceased to have any further involvement in aviation. At Dalmuir however, the Aircraft Design Office remained open and a series of military and civil aircraft types were produced. Sir William Beardmore had lost none of his interest in aviation and he correctly foresaw the passenger and cargo-carrying potential of aircraft and airships. Together, the aviation works at Inchinnan and Dalmuir provided the base upon which a first class aeronautical industry could be established on Clydeside.

In 1919 the Company produced an illustrated catalogue of no fewer than thirteen civil and military designs based mostly on wartime aircraft but including some completely new designs. The Company's attitude towards aviation is described in the catalogue

'... Definite air routes are already being established between different countries and between important industrial centres. This will stimulate the production of commercial aircraft , and it is the

intention of this firm to take such a part in the development of the services on these routes as shall be commensurate with its importance. The design and production of war machines will still be continued, but the firm with its world wide connection and experience, is well fitted to take up commercial aviation, while the experience gained during the war, in the design and manufacture of aeroplanes of all types and sizes, will prove invaluable in the new sphere. There are already several designs of commercial and long distance machines in hand and these should prove superior to anything so far produced. Few firms have facilities for the production of complete aeroplanes, the

One of two WBIIb aircraft which inaugurated the Renfrew to Croydon proving flights in September 1920.

The last Beardmore built airship, R36, emerges from the shed at Inchinnan in April 1921. A minimum ground crew of 300 persons was required to walk the airship out of the shed.

The four Beardmore built airships. From top to bottom No. 24, No. 27, R34 and R36. The R prefix was not adopted for airships until 1919.

majority being either purely aeroplane or purely engine manufacturers, but it is our policy to build Beardmore aeroplanes fitted with Beardmore engines and all fittings etc. to be of Beardmore manufacture. . .'

One of the most interesting new designs was the WBVIII, a large passenger carrying triplane capable of carrying 24 passengers and 5 crew. This unusual machine had two separate passenger fuselages slung on either side of a central nacelle which housed the cockpit and three crew as well as three Galloway Atlantic engines. The latter were under development at the Company's Dumfries works and had already been fitted to the first Beardmore V/1500. The other two crew members were assigned to the passenger compartments.[10]

At the International Aero Exhibition held at Olympia in July, Beardmore had on display a mock-up of a section of the passenger cabin from the airship R36 and a WBII styled as a two seat touring and sporting model. In 1920, the Company inaugurated the first Glasgow (Renfrew) to London (Croydon) scheduled air service operated by two WBIIb aircraft, developed from the WBII fighter reconnaissance aircraft. The first flight was on 17 September 1920. With a complement of only two including the pilot, it is unlikely that this service

was intended to be anything other than a demonstration of potential and after six weeks, the service was withdrawn.[11]

In the same year, Air Ministry sponsored competitions provided the impetus for two new aircraft designs, the first of which, the WBX, was an all metal two-seater powered by a 185 hp Beardmore engine. In August 1920, the only WBX ever built was taken by road from Dalmuir to Martlesham Heath in Suffolk where the competition was held. The aircraft was only flown once, on 16 August and withdrawn soon after proving less than satisfactory.

The second of the new designs, the WBIX, was a flying boat designed to carry ten passengers plus crew. '*Flight*' magazine stated that 'quite extraordinary interest attaches to the machine entered by Beardmore on account of its unusual construction, no less than because of its centre engine arrangement (four 200 hp Beardmores) with transmission to airscrews on the wings'.[12] However, when it was realised that the present rate of construction would not permit completion on time, work on the flying boat was abandoned after reaching an advanced state.

In the following year the Aviation Department was closed. The post-war boom had been short lived and the belief that aerial transportation was

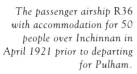

The passenger airship R36 with accommodation for 50 people over Inchinnan in April 1921 prior to departing for Pulham.

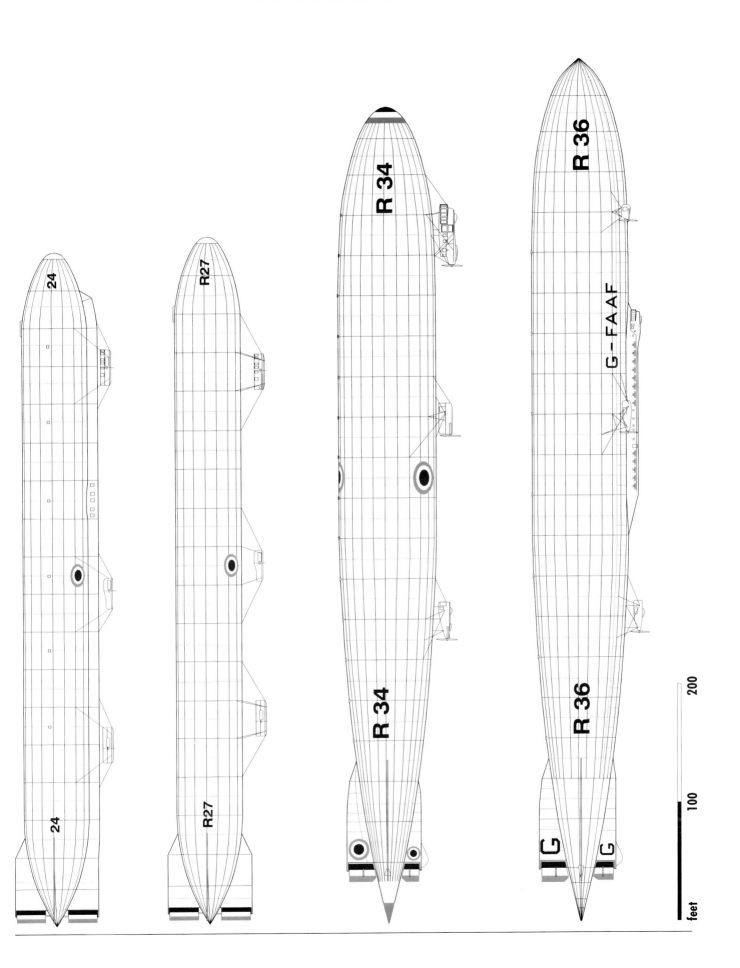

feet

200

100

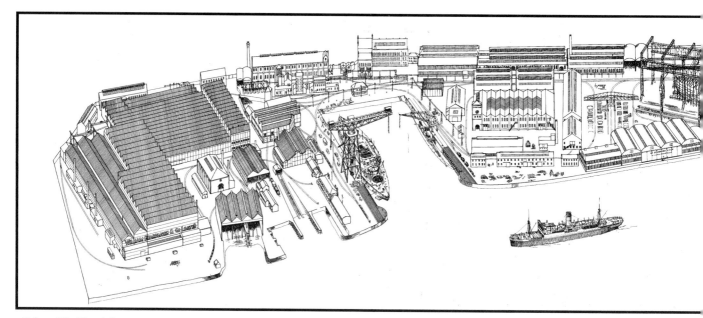

*Below. The Naval Construction
Works showing full development
of the site in 1921.*

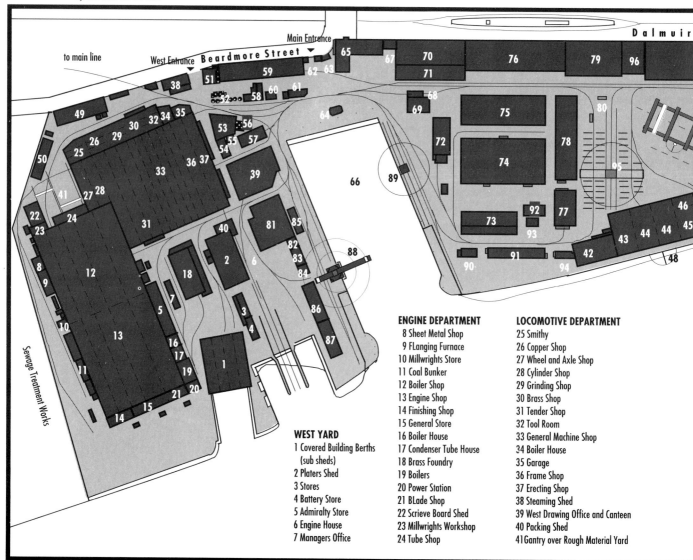

ENGINE DEPARTMENT

8 Sheet Metal Shop
9 FLanging Furnace
10 Millwrights Store
11 Coal Bunker
12 Boiler Shop
13 Engine Shop
14 Finishing Shop
15 General Store
16 Boiler House
17 Condenser Tube House
18 Brass Foundry
19 Boilers
20 Power Station
21 BLade Shop
22 Scrieve Board Shed
23 Millwrights Workshop
24 Tube Shop

LOCOMOTIVE DEPARTMENT

25 Smithy
26 Copper Shop
27 Wheel and Axle Shop
28 Cylinder Shop
29 Grinding Shop
30 Brass Shop
31 Tender Shop
32 Tool Room
33 General Machine Shop
34 Boiler House
35 Garage
36 Frame Shop
37 Erecting Shop
38 Steaming Shed
39 West Drawing Office and Canteen
40 Packing Shed
41 Gantry over Rough Material Yard

WEST YARD

1 Covered Building Berths
   (sub sheds)
2 Platers Shed
3 Stores
4 Battery Store
5 Admiralty Store
6 Engine House
7 Managers Office

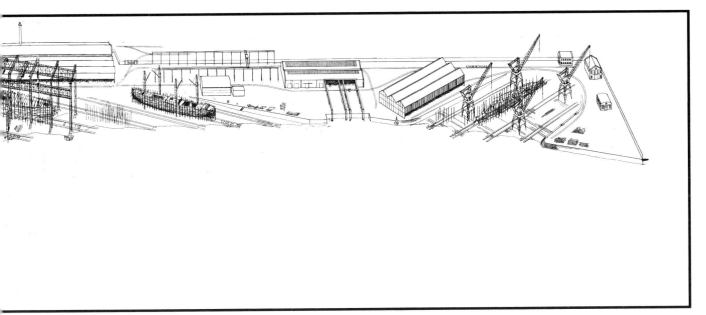

Above. An aerial perspective of the plan shown below.

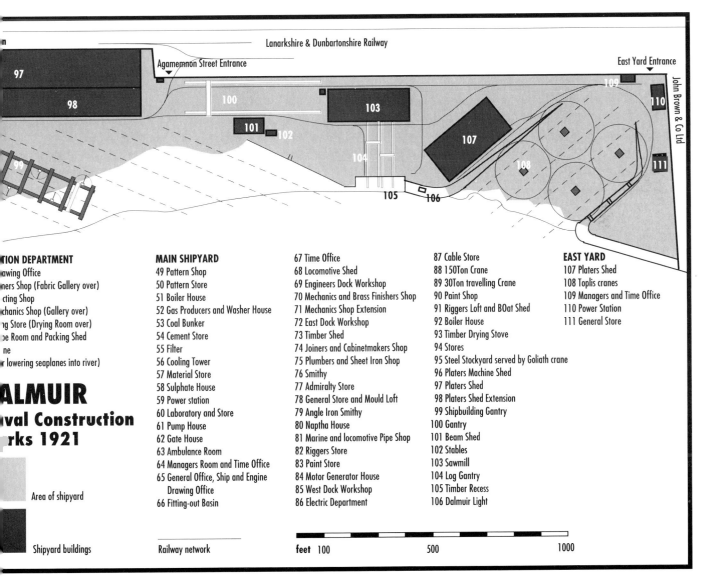

Lanarkshire & Dunbartonshire Railway

Agamemnon Street Entrance

East Yard Entrance

John Brown & Co Ltd

…TION DEPARTMENT
…rawing Office
…ers Shop (Fabric Gallery over)
…cting Shop
…chanics Shop (Gallery over)
…ng Store (Drying Room over)
…e Room and Packing Shed
…ne
…r lowering seaplanes into river)

…ALMUIR
…val Construction
…rks 1921

Area of shipyard

Shipyard buildings

Railway network

MAIN SHIPYARD
49 Pattern Shop
50 Pattern Store
51 Boiler House
52 Gas Producers and Washer House
53 Coal Bunker
54 Cement Store
55 Filter
56 Cooling Tower
57 Material Store
58 Sulphate House
59 Power station
60 Laboratory and Store
61 Pump House
62 Gate House
63 Ambulance Room
64 Managers Room and Time Office
65 General Office, Ship and Engine
   Drawing Office
66 Fitting-out Basin

67 Time Office
68 Locomotive Shed
69 Engineers Dock Workshop
70 Mechanics and Brass Finishers Shop
71 Mechanics Shop Extension
72 East Dock Workshop
73 Timber Shed
74 Joiners and Cabinetmakers Shop
75 Plumbers and Sheet Iron Shop
76 Smithy
77 Admiralty Store
78 General Store and Mould Loft
79 Angle Iron Smithy
80 Naptha House
81 Marine and locomotive Pipe Shop
82 Riggers Store
83 Paint Store
84 Motor Generator House
85 West Dock Workshop
86 Electric Department

87 Cable Store
88 150Ton Crane
89 30Ton travelling Crane
90 Paint Shop
91 Riggers Loft and BOat Shed
92 Boiler House
93 Timber Drying Stove
94 Stores
95 Steel Stockyard served by Goliath crane
96 Platers Machine Shed
97 Platers Shed
98 Platers Shed Extension
99 Shipbuilding Gantry
100 Gantry
101 Beam Shed
102 Stables
103 Sawmill
104 Log Gantry
105 Timber Recess
106 Dalmuir Light

EAST YARD
107 Platers Shed
108 Toplis cranes
109 Managers and Time Office
110 Power Station
111 General Store

feet 100   500   1000

Below. A job title unlikely to be encountered again.

imminent on a large scale had proved to be premature. Since the war, no aircraft orders had been received and the Company was in any case entering a period of financial uncertainty. Closure should not obscure the fact that Beardmore proposals for civil aircraft types were essentially on the right lines. Interest in aviation within the Company did not cease altogether and development work on advanced diesel aero engines continued at Parkhead.

In a separate development, the Beardmore Company was appointed to manage the Royal Air Force Reserve Flying School which was established at Renfrew in July 1923. This school which operated until closure in 1928, was run as an outpost of Dalmuir and was under the overall management of AJ Campbell.

AIRSHIPS

Early in 1919, the possibility of building two large airships annually seemed likely with Beardmore featuring in this programme. Indeed, there was confidence that the West of Scotland's contribution to the development of the airship would be on a par with the former's role in the building of ships.[13] In March 1919, the Admiralty placed orders for four R38 Class airships – Shorts 2 (R38 and R39), Beardmore 1 (R40) and Armstrong Whitworth 1 (R41).[14] These airships were the largest British designs so far with a cubic capacity of 2.75 million feet. Airships appear to have been close to the heart of Sir William Beardmore for at the Staff Victory Dinner given by the Company on 24 April 1919 he considered rigid airships 'to be the most interesting and important development of all'.[15]

After the war many interesting ideas were put forward for establishing commercial airship services. In the Autumn of 1919, a meeting took place in London between interested parties including Beardmore, Armstrong and Cunard in which routes to Holland, Scandinavia, Spain as well as a weekly transatlantic service and internal UK routes, were discussed. The possibility of building very large airships to establish Imperial air routes was also considered, although in the short term, nothing came of these proposals other than the flight of the R34 across the Atlantic as something of a trial run.[16]

Nevertheless, airships remained a matter of considerable debate and if they had their supporters, they certainly had their detractors.

Typical of the viewpoint adopted by the opponents of the airship service was that expressed by a Lt. Commander Kenworthy in a debate in the House of Commons over the Naval Estimates on 24 July 1919 –

'...the question of airships concerns the Admiralty, and I should like to ask the First Lord to give pause before he proceeds to relate the programme of airship building. These airships cost £350,000 each and there are great sheds which will be of doubtful value in the future. The reason is that aeroplanes and seaplanes are advancing in efficiency so rapidly that an airship will have about as much chance as a sailing ship has today with a cruiser. The analogy is this – that the sailing ship was useful for a certain time and then it became obsolete, and this is the same as the airship, which I believe will be dead in spite of non-inflammable gas or any other improvements ...'[17]

Uncertainty over the airship programme resulted in the cancellation of all R38 class airships on the 20 August 1919 with the exception of the R38 herself. In October 1919, airships and their stations were transferred from Admiralty to Air Ministry control with the belief that the latter would shortly produce concrete proposals for the future use of airships. It was agreed that the R36 should be completed as a civilian ship with passenger accommodation for fifty people and that two more airships should be built, the small experimental R80 by Vickers at Walney Island, and the large R38 at Cardington in the former Shorts works now taken over by the Air Ministry as the Royal Airship Works. At a meeting held in London on 4 February 1920 chaired by Air Commodore Maitland (with representatives from the constructors present including Mr Wallace of Beardmore's) various aspects of accommodation were on the agenda for the R33, R36 and R37. Sleeping accommodation, seating, cooking arrangements, heating and hot water supply, washing and sanitary arrangements, lighting and possible Board of Trade regulations governing the use of airships were discussed at length. Beardmore was asked to look into the making of experimental apparatus for generating steam from engine exhaust. and it was unanimously agreed that the matter was one of extreme urgency, and that no loss of time could be allowed in investigating the problem'.[18]

Following a rather lengthy conversion to

civilian use, the R36 first flew on 1 April 1921. She was given the registration G-FAAF and was completed with two forward power cars from the Zeppelin L71 each with a 260 hp Maybach engine. R36 was destined to have as disappointing a career, if less tragic, as some of her sisters. In June 1921, she was damaged while mooring at Pulham and spent the next four years retired in her shed. Early in 1925, refitting of the airship commenced at Pulham and a trial flight to Egypt was planned for the summer of that year. This work, which included the fitting of strain guages, was done as a test for structural stresses prior to the building of the very large airships R100 and R101. However, work on R 36 was not finished and she was broken up for scrap. Apart from work on the R36, the cancellation of the R40 left the Inchinnan works with nothing to do with the exception of the manufacture of the gas bags for the R38.

Although it was not yet the end of rigid airship development in Britain, it was the end for Inchinnan. Despite continued talk of the institution of commercial services, no definite policy was forthcoming from the Air Ministry who, with the acquisition of the Cardington Works, considered all other works superfluous to requirements. In 1921 the airship service was closed down and rigid airship flights did not resume again until 1925. In September 1921, the Air Ministry announced that Inchinnan Aerodrome was to be closed leaving Moorpark aerodrome at Renfrew as the only remaining Scottish civil airfield. On 12 October 1922, the land and buildings of the Inchinnan Airship Station were handed over to the Disposal and Liquidation Commission. On the 5 December 1922, the *Glasgow Herald* printed what was in effect the obituary for the works,

'it was created during the war under that veil of secrecy which enshrouded all the war work and although its great size and camouflaged appearance soon made it the most conspicuous object on the landscape for miles around, very little was known about the work for which it was intended. Only those associated with the work were allowed near it, and its secrets were guarded with scrupulous care . . . At one time there were proposals for the building of airships so much larger than the R34 that the shed would have to be extended for their construction but with the close of the war these proposals were departed from and it was found that

A six-cylinder Beardmore Tosi Supercharged diesel engine.

the shed could not be used to advantage for any postwar purposes. For a time it was hoped that it would be adapted for the construction of commercial aeroplanes, but the demand for aeroplanes of this kind, was not sufficient to justify Messrs Beardmore or the Air Board in undertaking such work on the extensive scale that would have been necessary if the undertaking were to meet with success . . .'

In April 1923 the works were sold to Murray McVinnie and Company ship chandlers, machinery and metal merchants who had recently purchased and disposed of the large airship shed at East Fortune near Edinburgh. The plant and machinery was auctioned in May 1923 and the Airship Shed, after a life of only seven years, was demolished later that year. [19] The remaining shops lay vacant until December 1927 when they were purchased by the India Tyre and Rubber Company. The 'Handley Page Shed' although much smaller than the airship shed was nevertheless a landmark for miles around and survived until demolished in 1982.

MARINE ENGINEERING

In 1918, the Company, in common with most other marine engineers, was again able to take-up and develop interesting ideas in ship propulsion which the war years had frozen. This interest, already expressed with little success in the gas engines of prewar days, concerned transmission systems and the introduction of the marine diesel.

The widespread introduction of the steam turbine to many classes of ship, highlighted the relative inefficiency of the turbine acting directly on the propeller shaft. The turbine had to revolve too slowly while the propeller revolved too quickly. The solution lay in transmission systems which

*Above. The Cameronia
photographed on 10 March
1921 during trials.*

*Below. The launch party of
the liner Tyrrhenia on 31
May 1921.
Lord Invernairn looks up at
the liner's bows while Lady
Invernairn prepares to press
the button which will activate
the launching triggers. The
Marquis of Graham with
bowler hat and brolly, stands
to the right.*

would enable the turbine to run more efficiently at several thousand revolutions per minute and the propeller, through a transmission system, to turn more efficiently at several hundred revolutions per minute. Beardmore investigated the three most promising methods available by which this could be achieved, the most successful of which turned out to be gearing. The use of gears initially took the form of single reduction gearing which eventually progressed to double reduction systems. The Dalmuir built passenger ship *Conte Rosso* was the first mercantile vessel of her size to

be fitted with double reduction gearing.

The other systems were electric and hydraulic transmission, for which the Company had taken out manufacturing licences as early as 1913. In the first – turbo electric drive – a turbine generator supplies current to induction motors which are coupled to the propeller shaft. Manufacturing rights were acquired from the Swedish Ljungström Company by the specially formed British Ljungström Marine Turbine Co Ltd. Turbines and motors were constructed and installed in the cargo vessel *Wulsty Castle* which was building at J Blumer's Sunderland shipyard for the Lancashire Shipping Company. This ship was completed in April 1918 to become the first British ship to be powered by turbo-electric machinery. After a period of repeated main machinery breakdowns, the *Wulsty Castle* was bought by Beardmore in 1920 as Beardmore claimed that the propulsion plant 'had not received fair treatment at the hands of the inefficient engineer in charge'.[20] Despite direct involvement by Beardmore, the engines remained unsatisfactory and the ship was laid up in the Bruges Canal for four years. In March 1925 the vessel was taken to the Vulcan Works at Stettin, where the original engines were removed and replaced with two three cylinder double-acting four-stroke Beardmore Tosi diesels built at Dalmuir. These engines were driven through a Vulcan clutch designed and fitted by the Vulcan shipyard. Sea trials of the *Wulsty*

Castle in this form, were conducted in the Elbe in August 1926.[21]

In 1916, when the Anchor Line first approached the shipyard in connection with the building of the *Tyrrhenia*, Ljungström turbo-electric machinery was specified for installation although the ship was completed with geared turbines.

The last transmission system investigated was known as the Föttinger Transformer, a hydraulic transmission system invented by Dr H Föttinger of the Vulcan Works. This system, in which a primary water wheel connected to the turbine delivers water to a secondary turbine wheel on the propeller shaft, was used extensively and successfully on German destroyers during the war although Beardmore appears not to have taken up their manufacturing rights.

By far the most significant development in the propulsion of merchant ships lay in the introduction of the diesel engine. In the 1914 edition of *'Lloyds Register'*, 297 diesel engined

A Glasgow tramcar travelling along Govan Road is dwarfed by the Cameronia in No3 graving dock at Govan for hull inspection prior to delivery in 1921. This was the longest graving dock on the Clyde but even this dock could not accept a ship with a beam greater than 83 feet.

ships of 250,000 gross tons are listed in comparison to the 1922 figure of 1,500,000 tons. This was still a small amount in contrast to the 51,500,000 tons propelled by reciprocating machinery and 8,000,000 tons steam turbine powered. However, to give some indication of the rise of the diesel, the 1930 figure had climbed to 9,000,000 tons while the other two remained static.

As early as 1911, the first diesel engines had gone to sea in commercial form in the twin screw cargo vessel *Selandia* built and engined by Burmeister & Wain of Copenhagen. A year later, the Barclay Curle built *Jutlandia*, became the first British motorship. The war years stifled further application of the diesel by British engine builders and after the end of hostilities, many yards including Beardmore, acquired licences to construct marine diesels of foreign design. It is quite significant that with the exception of the Doxford diesel, British yards played little part in the development of the marine diesel engine in complete contrast to the original contributions made with the reciprocating engine and steam turbine.

Beardmore approached the Italian firm Franco Tosi of Legnano, designers and builders of a successful marine diesel, and took out rights to the manufacture of their engine. At Dalmuir, the Company immediately set about the construction of a six cylinder four stroke single acting diesel of the Tosi type, developing a total of 1,250 bhp. Numerous detail improvements were made to the engine and after exhaustive shop trials, the engine was installed in the first of two small motorships *Pinzon*, which had been ordered from the firm by McAndrews of Liverpool. In January, the *Pinzon* ran successful trials which were concluded on Saturday 14 January when she made eight progressive runs on the measured mile off Skelmorlie working up to twelve knots. Various representatives from shipping lines and shipyards were on board *Pinzon* during the trials period and Beardmore was confident that further orders would follow.

In the main yard, the 16,000 ton *Cameronia* was launched on 23 December 1919 – by Lady Hermione Cameron of Lochiel – after only nine and a half months on the stocks, an achievement described by the *Marine Engineer* as noteworthy and elsewhere as a post war record for a ship of that size. Her sister ship *Tyrrhenia*, which was transferred from Anchor Line to Cunard Line

ownership shortly after she was laid down, had a slower building time, taking over one year to reach the launching stage. Nevertheless, at the luncheon held in the general offices after the launch of the *Cameronia*, Sir William Beardmore in complimentary mood, claimed that despite the introduction of the 47 hour week, only 9.14% of time had been lost in the Autumn period of 1919 by journeymen of all trades in the Shipbuilding Department compared with 11.9% lost in a comparable period of the previous year when the 54 hour week was worked. Overall, 6.4% of time had been lost throughout 1919 in comparison with a loss of 13% in 1913 the year of peak achievement by shipbuilders on Clydeside. Beardmore attributed this 'diligence and application to the later starting time in the morning and an increased interest in production'[22] He pointed out that the berth vacated by the *Cameronia* would be 'lined off and a new keel laid during the following day'. Referring to the uniqueness of his firm's ability to provide all of the materials, castings and forgings required in shipbuilding, he spoke of the 'magnificent opportunity for our workers... who have only to apply themselves diligently, keep good time, and abstain from all petty differences or disputes, leaving any big question that may arise to be determined by arbitration, and thus ensure steady work and good wages for themselves for many years to come. There can thus be no question of unemployment here.'[23]

The two Lloyd Sabaudo passenger ships were laid down in January 1920, the first to be launched being the *Conte Rosso* in February 1921. On the first attempt at launching, the *Conte Rosso* only managed to move twenty feet down the ways and as the tide was waning, she had to be blocked up where she lay. The launch was re-scheduled for 10 February on which date she entered the water without difficulty.

In the early 1920s, a series of prolonged strikes hit the shipbuilding industry when the employers sought to reduce the spiralling cost of production by the removal of special wartime and post war bonuses. On 1 December 1920, the joiners were the first to strike over the proposed removal of bonuses of twelve shillings per week – not a trivial sum considering the average shipyard wage was £4. Four thousand joiners were affected by the action which lasted for nine months and was settled in favour of the employers by the immediate

Opposite. A Heath Robinson cartoon of the shipbuilding yard at Dalmuir commissioned for Beardmore News *in August 1921.*

removal of six shillings per week followed by the further removal of three shillings in October and three shillings in December. The joiners returned to work on 26 August 1921.[24] Naturally, all vessels under construction were considerably delayed. The *Cameronia* which should have been completed in January 1921, sailed to Cherbourg for completion of joinery work and was not ready for service until March. After the launch of the *Largs Bay* in June 1921, Sir William – now Lord Invernairn of Strathnairn since being raised to the peerage in the 1921 New Years honours list in full recognition of his services to the country – spoke of the need to lower the costs of production.

> 'I am glad to say that the cost of steel – the essential material used in the construction of a ship – had fallen in price by £4 per ton. I am also glad to say that shipyard workers had agreed to a reduction in their wages of something like six shillings and ninepence per week, and hope and believe that the engineers would now see their way to accept a similar reduction . . . what killed the post-war boom in shipbuilding was the high cost of production, and the shorter working week had contributed very materially to this'.[25]

At the launching of the *Esperance Bay* in December 1921, Beardmore, referring to the strikes, said

Above. Painters working on the bow of the Tyrrhenia. *Approximately 60 tons of paint was used during fitting-out.*

Tyrrhenia in the dock at Dalmuir during the last stages of fitting out.

'Strikes are for the moment, I am pleased to say, suspended . . .'[26]

Spiralling costs had forced the suspension of the *Conte Verde* on 8 February 1921, and it was only after the costs of production had come down and £600,000 of Government money under the Trade Facilities Act, was made available for the building of the *Conte Verde,*[27] that work was able to recommence on 4 March 1922. Even then, strikes in the shipyard and engine departments prevented work beginning in earnest until May.

The lock-out of the engineers which started on 11 March 1922 and lasted for thirteen weeks, was over the issue of overtime payments although it developed into a managerial rights issue. The shipbuilding unions struck on 28 March 1922 over the removal of war bonuses totalling sixteen shillings and six pence per week. This strike ended on 8 May with the men returning largely on the employers terms with the bonus being removed more gradually than first proposed. The other major lock-out of this period started on 31 April 1923 when 30,000 boilermakers were locked-out over the issue of night shift and overtime payments. This lock-out lasted thirty weeks ending on 26 November 1923.[28] The table on this page lists typical weekly wages of time workers in shipyards and is reproduced from the *Shipbuilder* of 1921.

Meanwhile, the order position at Dalmuir was deteriorating prompting Lord Invernairn to comment in December 1921, 'One must look to the immediate future with considerable anxiety. We have not booked a contract at Dalmuir for many months. During the last two or three years,

TYPICAL WEEKLY WAGES OF TIME WORKERS 1921			
	July 1914	January 1920	January 1921	Amount of War and Post war Bonuses
	s d	s d	s d	s d
Shipwrights	41 6	84 4	91 0	49 6
Plumbers	41 6	84 4	91 0	49 6
Joiners	40 6	83 3	89 11	49 5
Frame Turners	39 0	81 6	88 2	49 2
Platers	39 0	81 6	88 2	49 2
Blacksmiths	39 0	81 6	88 2	49 2
Fitters	39 0	81 6	88 2	49 2
Angle-Iron Smiths	38 0	80 5	87 1	49 1
Painters	38 0	80 5	87 1	49 1
Drillers	37 4	79 8	86 2	54 10
Caulkers and Cutters	37 0	79 4	86 0	49 0
Riveters	37 0	79 4	86 0	49 0
Helpers (Blocks and boards)	35 0	77 1	83 9	48 9
Helpers (Outside)	32 0	73 8	80 4	48 4
Holders-up	31 6	73 1	79 9	48 3

ships have cost three times as much as the prewar figure.[29]

The brief few years of the boom had been busy at Dalmuir and in 1921 the yard achieved, for the first and last time, the distinction of building and engining more vessels than any other Clydeside yard. So rapid was the downturn in trade however, that by the end of that year the order position was bleak; only one ship was on the stocks at the main yard and that was the suspended hull of the *Conte Verde*. Worse was to follow. In November 1921, the yard received a major set-back with the suspension and subsequent cancellation of an

Bottom. Tyrrhenia *on trials in June 1922*

order to build a 48,000 ton battlecruiser for the Navy. As this order would have been of immense significance to the shipyard had it remained in force, the origins and cancellation of this warship under the terms of the Washington Treaty are worth closer examination.

THE WASHINGTON TREATY

By 1920, the prospect of a new round of capital ship orders was likely, heralding yet another arms race. After the end of the war in 1918, much discussion took place over the issue of Imperial Defence. Within the Admiralty the role of the battleship and the desirability of building them at all, particularly in light of recent advances made in aerial and submarine warfare, was questioned. However, whatever the merits of the debate were, the balance of opinion lay in favour of the battleship continuing as the principal instrument of seapower. The real spur in pushing for new construction however, lay in the existence of the large American and Japanese naval building programmes which, for the Royal Navy threatened with the possibility of a greater naval force, made

the issue one of when and not if. The British capital ships designed in response to this challenge during 1920/21 were spectacular and significantly better on both offensive and defensive capabilities, than the most recently completed British capital ship, the battlecruiser *Hood*. Within the Admiralty, it was hoped that four battlecruisers mounting sixteen inch guns could be laid-down in 1921 to be followed a year later by four battleships mounting eighteen inch guns. This became official policy and on 3 September 1921, invitations to tender for the four battlecruisers, known at this time by their design prefix G3 were given to Armstrong, Beardmore, John Brown, Cammell Laird, Fairfield, Harland & Wolff, Swan Hunter and Vickers. The successful firms were Beardmore (£3,786,332), John Brown (£3,879,000), Fairfield (£3,900,000) and Swan Hunter (£3,977,175).[30] These figures included a fixed establishment charge and a profit of £700,000. The first three ships were ordered on 26 October 1921 with a specified completion date of 1 November 1924. Beardmore's order was placed on 1 November 1921, although the order for the

In the short space of 15 years, the development of the battleship resulted in the design of very large ships. This is amply demonstrated by three Beardmore battleship orders, the Agamemnon of 1907, the Ramillies of 1917 and the G3 of 1921 which although ordered was not built.

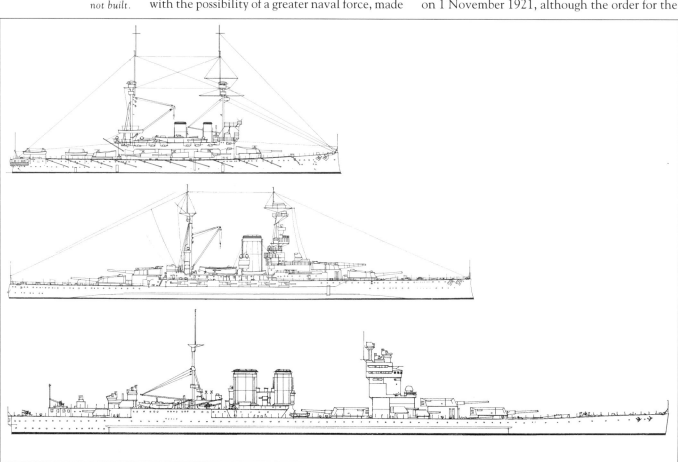

The Esperance Bay *built for the Commonwealth Government Line undergoing trials on 11 July 1922.*

main propelling machinery was placed with Vickers in similar fashion to the Swan Hunter ship whose machinery went to Parsons.[31]

While advance ordering of materials and preparations to commence work on these ships were in progress, events were about to place the wisdom of these orders in doubt. Throughout 1921, concern was voiced in the United States over the escalating dimensions of the naval race in which they found themselves particularly as the American capital ships, which had been designed several years previously, did not compare favourably with their more formidable Japanese and British counterparts. At American behest, the major naval powers were invited to attend a conference in Washington which first met on 12 November with a remit to explore possible ways of limiting the naval building programmes. After six days, the direction of the conference was clear enough for the Admiralty in London to issue notice to the four yards concerned to suspend the battlecruiser contracts pending the outcome of the conference. By early February 1922, the Washington Conference was over and a treaty signed. Limitation was agreed upon and complex ratios affecting classes of warships relative to a

Below. The Italian liner Conte Rosso *on trials on 14 August 1922.*

Lord Invernairn on the bridge of the Conte Rosso *together with the Marquis de La Penne, managing director of the Lloyd Sabaudo Line. Lord and Lady Invernairn sailed on the* Conte Rosso's *maiden voyage from Genoa to Buenos Aires in March/April 1922.*

particular country agreed. There would be no new battleships or battlecruisers for a period of ten years – and so the battleship building 'holiday' began. In order to restore parity of numbers in compliance with treaty conditions, Britain was allowed to build two 'Treaty' battleships of 35,000 tons. While the Government welcomed the outcome of the Conference for financial reasons, the future for the warship builders in Britain looked decidedly leaner. Not only would there be no capital ships ordered for ten years apart from these two, the reality was that British maritime power was circumscribed if not yet eclipsed. Financially drained by the First World War, Britain was now a signatory to a treaty which pegged the size of her navy to that of the United States. For the first time in over one hundred years, the size of the Royal Navy was equalled by a foreign fleet. The implications for the warship builders were clear.

The four battlecruisers were cancelled outright on 13 February 1922. The winning and subsequent loss of these contracts was hailed as a triumph and then as a disaster for Clydeside and in the case of Dalmuir came as a grave blow parallelled within the firm by the impact on the Armour Plate and Gun Shops at Parkhead. Speaking in December 1921 when the contracts were in suspension, Sir William said,

'My principal regret is our inability to give employment to many thousands of men, who in the ordinary course, would have been engaged in work necessitated by these contracts. . . I trust

Opposite. The magnificent music room on the Conte Rosso. *The interior design was carried out by the Florentine firm of Coppede. Italian artisans were brought over to Dalmuir to work on the panels.*

The Conte Rosso

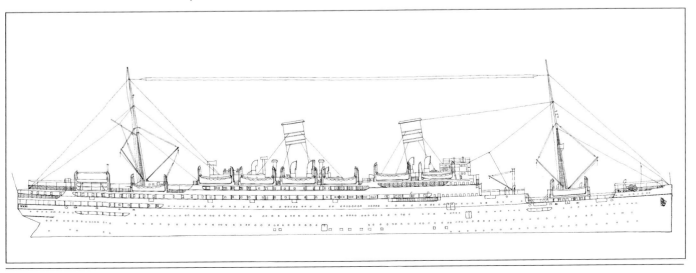

14 BUILDING BERTHS ACCOMMODATING VESSELS up to 1,000 ft in LENGTH

SHIPBUILDING
& MARINE ENGINEERING
WILLIAM
BEARDMORE
AND COMPANY · LIMITED
SHIPYARDS, DALMUIR. SCOTLAND.   LONDON, 36 VICTORIA St, S.W.I

The Lloyd Sabaudo liner Conte Rosso about to leave Dalmuir and make her way down river.

notwithstanding the suspension of these contracts – for it is not definite yet, that possibly ships of a smaller size may be built[32]

The reference to the smaller battleships is explained by a letter sent in confidence from the Admiralty to the four shipyards stating that two Treaty battleships would definitely be ordered implying perhaps that these new orders would be limited to tender from the four previously successful shipyards. In the event, when tenders were invited, it was from all the naval yards. The orders for the new ships were placed on 1 January 1923 with Cammell Laird (*Rodney*) and Armstrong Whitworth (*Nelson*). *The Engineer* of 5 January 1923, stated that there was surprise that Clydeside received no order for these battleships after winning three out of the four cancelled ships. When questions were asked in the House of

Commons, the Prime Minister suggested that the winning tenders had been put in at a loss while the others had not. The Clydeside tenders were thought to be as much as £180,000 over the successful ones.[33]

In their issue of October 1921, *Shipbuilding & Shipping Record* estimated that the four battlecruiser contracts would give employment to 5,000 men in the first two months of 1922 rising to 25,000 the following year. About 500 firms would be involved and of the total contract price of £30 million, a substantial portion would go in wages.

Beardmore's battlecruiser contract was alive for only three weeks during which time no steel work would have been carried out either in the shops or on the berth, although advanced ordering of materials and berth preparation would have taken place. Expenditure of £2,700 is recorded against the contract in the Company's accounts.

Opposite. In confident mood: this striking Art Deco advert of the early 1920s portrays a liner under construction at Dalmuir. The proportions of the ship have been greatly exaggerated.

Guests at the launch of the Pinzon on 18 January 1922. Left to right: Captain Celli, Engineering Captain Onyon, Mr Jones, Mr Richardson, General Trenchard, Mr Simpson, Miss Celli, Lady Weir, Mr Campbell and Lord Weir. The lady to the extreme left is not identified.

During 1922, the last tankers for the British Tanker Company were completed along with the *Esperance Bay* and the *Conte Rosso*. Speaking at the launch of the *British Commerce* on 26 May, Beardmore said that the first of the tankers had been delivered six weeks ahead of contract, the second was ten weeks late, the third fourteen weeks late and the fourth (*British Commerce*) was twenty weeks late. The latter vessel had been delayed by the engineers lock-out while the two previous ships had been held up by the joiners strike. *British Merchant*, the last to be launched, was delayed on her building slip by four months due to the lock-out. The East Yard was left with no work whatsoever.

The Company's first two diesel powered ships ordered in 1920, the *Pinzon* and *Pizarro*, were in progress with the first launched and the other

The motor ship Pizarro during trials on 3 January 1923.

nearing completion. The much delayed *Conte Verde*, the largest ship launched at Dalmuir that year, went down the ways on 21 October. Of the above mentioned, the *Conte Rosso* was the largest mercantile vessel yet completed at Dalmuir and was said to surpass all other post-war liners in the luxury of her passenger accommodation. The following extract from the '*Glasgow Herald*' of 15 February 1922, is testimony to the magnificence of the *Conte Rosso*'s interior.

'The entrance hall in the first class public rooms is in the style of the Italian Renaissance in oak and mahogany. Hand carvings, inlaid works, tapestry and stained glass play a part in the general scheme. The library is in the style of the Tuscan Renaissance of polished walnut, finely carved and inlaid. A frieze runs round the sides and there are some fifty set and landscape paintings embodied in the scheme. A music room is also provided in the Pompeiian style. The upper saloon is seated for seventy four in tables of two, four or six persons, is in the style of the Italian Renaissance slightly modified in some details. Round the sides is a dado richly carved and with tooled and gilt leather panels. Two large pictures of war episodes in the life of Conte Rosso recall the history of the man after whom the vessel is named. . . .'

The interior decorations of the first class public rooms on the ship were designed by the Florentine firm of Coppede. Italian artists were brought over to Dalmuir to work on and install many of the fittings. The *Conte Rosso* was also the first merchant ship to employ a ring main for the lighting circuits, this practice having been previously confined to warships. In March 1922, Lord and Lady Invernairn sailed on the *Conte Rosso*'s maiden voyage from Genoa to Santos and Buenos Aires.

In contrast to the magnificence of the shipyard's most recent production, the order position deteriorated rapidly throughout 1922 and only one minor order was secured. This was for the sludge boat *Henry Ward* for London County Council which was won for a contract price of £48,000 in December of that year. By that time the only other work in the yard was the fitting-out of the *Conte Verde* and the *Pizarro*. The following year both these vessels ran successful trials, the *Conte Rosso* in particular, easily exceeding her contract speed of 18.5 knots by making 20.15 knots on the measured mile off Skelmorlie. Highly

favourable 24 hour fuel consumption trials on the Irish Sea took place on 8 and 9 April after which the ship returned to the Tail-of-the-Bank for refuelling. On 10 April, she sailed for Genoa with Lord Invernairn, Douglas Vickers and the Marquis de la Penne, of the Lloyd Sabaudo Line, on board. At Genoa the ship's double reduction gearing was examined and found to be in perfect condition. On 21 April, the *Conte Verde* sailed on her maiden voyage to Buenos Aires.

A depressing note was sounded in *Shipbuilding & Shipping Record* which commented that workers returning from their annual holiday – Fair Fortnight – would be doing so to a river which had only half the amount of work in hand by comparison with the same time the previous year. Translated into numbers the comparison was 106 vessels instead of 238.[34] The depressed state of shipbuilding continued in 1923 and at Dalmuir this was poignantly underlined in choosing a berth for the construction of the *Henry Ward* – all fourteen were available.

Dalmuir shipyard was not the only cause for concern within the Beardmore Company. The trade depression was proving particularly difficult in general following the all but total collapse of the demand for armaments upon which they had so recently been dependent. The diversification pursued over the past few years was not an adequate substitute and in the Company's annual report for the year, an inkling was given of severe financial difficulties ahead.

At Dalmuir the quest for economy and the reduction of overheads was pursued vigorously when, in October 1923, A J Campbell, attended the Valuation Appeal Court in Glasgow claiming a 33.3% reduction on Dalmuir shipyard's assessed rateable valuation. Speaking as the principal witness for his own as well as other yards in his capacity as President of the Shipbuilding Employers' Federation in Scotland, Campbell gave the following statistics in support of the case for rates reduction;

'On the River Clyde there were 137 vacant shipbuilding berths, 66 berths were occupied by vessels which were in progress and 15 berths by vessels on which work was suspended. All over the country the members of the Shipbuilding Employers' Federation had 389 vacant berths, 155 occupied by vessels in progress and 56 on which vessels were held up. In 40 shipbuilding and 127

engineering establishments on the Clyde, the average prewar number of workers employed was 96,158, and the aggregate of the highest employed subsequent to 1914 was 152,891. The average for the first three months of this year -1923- was only 50,400 while the percentage of unemployment in the shipbuilding trades all over Scotland was 39.4.[35]

On 12 October, the plight of the shipbuilding industry attracted the attention of the *Daily Mail* which in addition to printing similar statistics to those quoted by Campbell, added that the present order position on Clydeside was the worst for thirty-six years. The average weekly wage bill at Dalmuir, which as recently as 1921 had been £36,000, was reduced to a mere £8,400.[36]

The chronic order position eased in the last half of 1923 when an order for two vessels, the *Arkoona* and *Allara* for the Adelaide Steamship Company, was booked in June. In October, a 2,000 ton icebreaker for the Latvian government, *Krisjanis Valdemars*, was ordered, while in November, the Anglo Saxon Petroleum Company placed an order for a 2,250 ton tanker, *Carlota*. In the same month the contract to recondition the *Empress of France* (built in the yard as the *Alsatian*) was won involving conversion of the ship to oil from coal burning as well as improvements to the passenger accommodation. In 1924 the flow of orders continued with two channel steamers, *Hebble* and *Rye* for the LMS Railway Company, a further steamer, *Ulooloo*, for the Adelaide

A Great Eastern 4-6-0 locomotive at the head of the fitting-out basin in 1920. *Cameronia* is almost complete to the left while *Tyrrhenia* is just visible underneath the 150 ton crane.

Steamship Company and three additional tankers for the Anglo Saxon Company, *Conchita*, *Cassandra* and *Chepita*. While these orders kept the shipyard and engine works occupied, it is doubtful if they did anything to alleviate the precarious financial position emerging at Dalmuir. Speaking at the Company's Annual Meeting in June 1925, Lord Invernairn referred to the extreme difficulty and anxiety of the past year mentioning a number of orders which had been taken on towards the end of 1923 and early 1924 which were 'at prices. . . wholly unremunerative'.

Welcome news was received in May 1924 when the contract for another prestigious passenger ship for the Lloyd Sabaudo Line was announced. This ship, the *Conte Biancamano* was at 24,000 tons, the largest of the trio of Italian liners built at Dalmuir during the 1920s and would almost certainly have been followed by a fourth, the *Conte Grande* of 30,000 tons, had it not been for Mussolini's policy of favouring Italian shipyards.

All the ships on order, except the Italian and Latvian vessels, were launched in 1924 without new contracts being won to replace them. The apparent success of the diesel installation of the *Pinzon* and *Pizarro* brought no immediate work to the engine shops and it was not until 1924 that an order for a Beardmore Tosi six cylinder 600 bhp diesel was received for the cargo vessel *Silurian* building at the Blythswood yard.[37]

THE FINAL YEARS: 1924 – 1930

The closure of the Aviation Department in 1921 proved to be for a relatively short time and in 1924, sufficient interest was expressed in several Air Ministry inspired projects to justify reopening. The first of these projects to reach fruition was an entrant in the 1924 Light Plane Competition at Lympne aerodrome. WS Shackleton, was engaged in 1924 as chief aircraft designer at Dalmuir and immediately set about the design and construction of a very small monoplane aircraft powered by an 1100cc Bristol Cherub engine.[1] In this task Shackleton was well qualified having designed the joint winner of the previous year's competition for the Air Navigation & Engineering Company (ANEC). Shackleton's 1924 design designated the WBXXIV but known as the 'Wee Bee' was successful emerging as overall winner against eighteen other aircraft on 4 October. The Wee Bee went on display at Wembley and Olympia later in the year but no orders for the aircraft were received.[2] In February the Company announced an order for two fighter aircraft for the Latvian Government for whom the shipyard was currently building an icebreaker.

The only WBXXIV ever built, the Wee Bee won the 1924 Light aeroplane Competition but no follow on orders were received. The Wee Bee is seen here at Renfrew in 1924.

The fighter was designated the WBXXVI, a two-seat biplane with a maximum speed of 148 mph and fitted with three Beardmore Farquhar machine guns. One of the aircraft was built by late December 1925 and this machine was put through a series of tests by the Company's chief test pilot Captain AN Kingwill. According to *Flight* the aircraft emerged from these trials with flying colours.[3] However, the truth was that the aircraft, although in posession of exceptional low speed handling characteristics, was underpowered. The Latvians chose not to proceed any further with this project and yet another promising development was at an end. At much the same time that the Latvian order was announced, two further designs were prepared which, like so many of the aircraft so far described, were destined never to be built. One was a single seat fighter – a strut braced parasol monoplane, the other a two seat reconnaissance seaplane – a monoplane with strut bracing to the floats and wings.[4]

However, the most significant reason for the reopening of the Aviation Department is probably found in the acquisition, in 1924, of the British

manufacturing rights to the Rohrbach system of aircraft construction.[5] During the First World War, Dr Adolph Rohrbach had worked for the Zeppelin Staaken Company concentrating on the aircraft activities of the airship builder. Rohrbach pioneered all-metal stressed-skin construction and after the war produced a number of advanced designs which virtually established the pattern for modern aircraft construction. However, Rohrbach's work was in contravention of the Treaty of Versailles and at least one of his aircraft – an advanced four engined airliner – was ordered to be broken-up by the Allied Control Commission. In addition to a Berlin plant, Rohrbach opened a factory in Denmark where he established the Rohrbach Metal Aeroplan Company A/S in Copenhagen.

Aircraft built under this system employed the light alloy Duralumin for all parts of the structure and the techniques of assembly resembled those employed in shipbuilding where plates, angles and channels are riveted together. This made the construction of very large, strong aircraft possible. The securing of the Rohrbach manufacturing

rights had been preceeded by an order from the Air Ministry in 1923 for a large experimental landplane to be built by this system. In 1924 a further order for two Rohrbach ROIV seaplanes was placed with Beardmore. The first of the two seaplane orders was not built at Dalmuir however but assembled at Copenhagen from parts made in Berlin and flown to the Marine Aircraft Experimental Establishment at Felixtowe on 18 September 1925. This aircraft served as a pattern for the second aircraft, known as the *Inverness*, which was not completed at Dalmuir until November 1928. This machine was lowered into the Clyde for the first time on 28 November and taken in tow down river to Roseneath where the first of a series of trial flights commenced two days later.[6] Both flying boats proved to be a disappointment and trials of the Dalmuir built version were halted in 1929 and the aircraft subsequently broken up.

In March 1926, the Company appointed Squadron Leader Rollo de Haga Haig as outside manager of the Aviation Department with responsibility for test flights, aircraft delivery and

The WBXXVI a two seat fighter built for the Latvian Government. Despite completing satisfactory trials, this aircraft did not go into production.

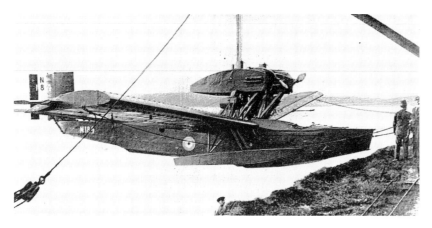

Top. Inverness – the Dalmuir built flying boat is lowered into the Clyde at Dalmuir for the first time on 28 November 1928

Above. The men and women of the Aviation Department who built the Inverness *and* Inflexible *photographed on 23 December 1927*

client liaison. This post was an indication of the firm's growing aeronautical activities.[7] The Rohrbach landplane, which was built at Dalmuir and transported in sections with difficulty to Martlesham Heath, was a very large experimental aircraft with a wing span of nearly 160 feet – the largest span of any aircraft built in Britain until the *Bristol Brabazon* in 1953. The *Inflexible*, as the aircraft was named, conformed in general to the Rohrbach principle although Shackleton made numerous detail changes. The *Inflexible* was assembled at the Aircraft Armament & Experimental Establishment at Martlesham Heath where she was nick-named the *'Incredible'*. Following static tests she was flown for the first time on 5 March 1928. The aircraft made an appearance at the RAF display at Hendon on 30 June and in the following year, made a couple of visits to air displays. She reputedly flew and handled well despite being rather underpowered.

Described as 'structurally fascinating' the *Inflexible* ended her days in 1930 when she was dismantled and left in the open as an experiment to test the corrosive action of the elements against the airframe.[8]

No further Air Ministry contracts were forthcoming following the *Inverness* and *Inflexible* experiments and the Company, by now in the midst of a serious financial crisis, did not possess the means to develop and extend the recently gained expertise in advanced construction techniques.

The last order undertaken in the Aviation Department before closure, is worthy of mention as in many ways it typifies the attitude and aspirations of the Beardmore Company – a commitment to novel and interesting ideas which for one reason or another, were destined to have little or no future whatsoever. This order was for part of a monorail system designed by the Glasgow engineer George Bennie who had the vision of linking cities in Britain with his railplane. Bennie claimed that the railplane would cut the travel time between Glasgow and Edinburgh to twenty minutes for a fare of three shillings and ninepence. Interest was shown in the possibility of a link between Blackpool and Southport while much later, proposals to employ the system at the 1938 Empire Exhibition in Glasgow were considered although not acted upon. At Dalmuir the Aviation Shops were entrusted with the construction of the aerodynamically shaped passenger car resembling an aircraft fuselage, which had an airscrew at either end. A 426 yard long experimental stretch of track was erected over the LNER railway line at Milngavie on the outskirts of Glasgow and the first trial run took place on 4 July 1930.[9] Despite the interest shown in the system, the Bennie Railplane was destined to become no more than a local curiosity and something of a landmark until it was demolished in 1956.

Under the rationalisation of the Company's activities, the Aviation Department at Dalmuir was closed finally in 1929. Aero engine development did continue at Parkhead under the control of Alan E L Chorlton which resulted in a series of large six cylinder in-line engines. Parallel development of a pioneering diesel aero engine at Parkhead resulted in the 'Tornado' which was fitted on the ill-fated airship R101.

In 1925, the Naval Estimates which had been cut back dramatically after 1918, revived slightly

Above. The great size of the Inflexible is clear in this view of her fully erected in the aviation sheds at Dalmuir. She was later dismantled and taken in sections to Martlesham Heath where she was put through a series of test flights.

Middle. The Inflexible assembled at Martlesham Heath in 1929

The wooden frame of the Benny Railplane under construction in the Aviation sheds at Dalmuir in 1929.

Above. The Bennie Railplane and the 426 yard length of track erected at Milngavie in 1930.

The aviation sheds and shipbuilding gantry from the south bank of the river during the 1920s.

when the Admiralty won a battle against the Chancellor of the Exchequer, Winston Churchill, to initiate a building programme of 10,000 ton 'Treaty' cruisers, later known as the County Class. In the first round of orders, Beardmore succeeded in winning the machinery contract for the *Cornwall* which was to be built at Devonport Dockyard. In contrast, John Brown received orders for two cruisers and Fairfield one. However in the following year, with tenders invited for a second batch, Beardmore won the contract to build the *Shropshire*, the first warship to be ordered and built in the yard in almost eight years. These cruiser contracts constituted the first naval orders to be placed with private builders since the Armistice with the exception of the two Treaty battleships

Nelson and *Rodney*. This building programme had originally been presented to the Government in the winter of 1923, partly in recognition of the depressed state of the naval shipbuilding yards. However, the Labour Government, which took office in January 1924, rejected it.

In 1927 the Company was again successful in winning two (*Olympus* and *Orpheus*) of the six submarines in the Odin class although the Admiralty required to have a bankers guarantee of £50,000 for the due completion of these vessels. This was arranged with the National Bank of Scotland.

Although only three warship orders had been placed with the yard in eight years, overall, Beardmore probably fared no better or worse than any of the other private warship yards during the 1920s and the Admiralty did attempt to share out what orders it was allowed to place. In recognition of the difficulties faced by the warship yards, an agreement was reached between them in 1925 for the sharing of such contracts as were available. This was not to Beardmore's advantage when, under the 1928 Programme, the yard was well placed to receive an order for two B class destroyers. However, despite a less competitive tender, the contract went to Hawthorn Leslie, it being argued that Beardmore already had two submarines.[10]

At a meeting of the board at Parkhead, Lord Invernairn made some rather outspoken comments about the state of industry claiming that in 90% of cases, producers of iron, steel, ships and

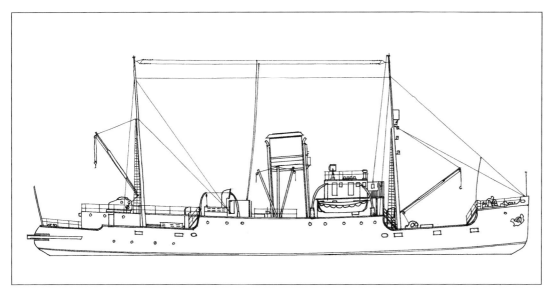

The Latvian icebreaker Krisjanis Valdemars

locomotives could not compete with their foreign counterparts. He listed the causes of this predicament as high taxation, high wages, short working hours, low output, the high cost of railway freights, dock charges and the high cost of fuel.[11]

If there appeared to be some movement in warship orders, merchant orders were again severely depressed. A J Campbell raised the issue of the shipbuilding depression in his inaugural speech in September 1925 when he became President of the Institution of Engineers and Shipbuilders in Scotland.

> 'Today there are about 96 shipyards in Britain. In 30 of these there is not a single keel laid. In 15, work in hand is rapidly nearing completion while the remainder are barely occupied beyond a quarter of their capacity. This situation is partly understood when it is realised that there are now 20% more berths in this country since before the war and that only 28% of these are occupied. The percentage of unemployed workmen is between 30 and 40%. In 1913 we built about 60% of the world's output, while at present this figure has dropped to 46%'.[12]

In their annual report the following month, the Committee of Lloyds Register of Shipping added to the gloomy statistics describing the situation as the 'most serious in living memory'.

By way of explaining at least some of the contributory factors the report continued:

The County Class cruiser Shropshire was the last surface warship to be built at Dalmuir.

The Canadian Pacific liner
Duchess of Atholl *fitting-*
out on 29 December 1927.

'On the one hand there was a large amount of surplus tonnage afloat. This was brought into existence by the extraordinary exertions of shipbuilders, particularly in the United States of America, under the compelling influence of war. On the other hand there was a serious shrinkage in the volume of the world's ocean trade as compared with prewar times. These conditions have combined to reduce freights below a paying level, but have failed to bring a corresponding reduction in the cost of production and operation of ships, thus rendering the position of shipowners and shipbuilders one of unexampled difficulty.'[13]

By the end of 1925, all the vessels on order at Dalmuir with one exception, had been delivered including the *Conte Biancamano* and the *Krisjanis Valdemars*. Despite the dearth of orders at the yard, the *Conte Biancamano*, the largest vessel built in the UK that year, was nevertheless built in the remarkably short time of 18 months from keel laying to trials, again underlining the ability of this yard to build rapidly. During her trials she developed 25,600 shp driven through double reduction gearing for a speed of over 21 knots. This gearing was the largest installation of its type

so far fitted in a merchant vessel. An article on this ship printed in *Engineering* claimed that the interior decoration and furnishings of her public rooms was on a scale 'unsurpassed in any vessel . . .'[14] With the departure of the *Conte Biancamano* for Genoa on 7 November, employment in the yard was reduced dramatically when two thousand men were paid off. The only vessel remaining was the *John Perring*, another 1,000 ton sludge boat for London County Council which had been laid down in July. And so, for the second time within the space of a few years, this great naval yard had been reduced to one order for a sludge boat.

In February 1926, the Companhia Nacional de Navegaco Costiera of Rio de Janerio, placed an order for three twin screw motorships, *Itapé, Itaquicé* and *Itanagé* to be propelled by Beardmore diesels. In June, Canadian Pacific, developing the North Atlantic trade, placed orders for two 'M' class intermediate liners on Clydeside. The *Duchess of Atholl* went to Beardmore and the *Duchess of Bedford* went to John Brown, who subsequently received orders for two further vessels of this type. Despite receiving the order to build the cruiser *Shropshire* in the Spring of 1926, she could not be laid down until February 1927 because of the coal strike and other trade disputes. Although prospects for the yard had improved, that summer the continuing unsatisfactory level of trade exacerbated by the coal strike caused Dalmuir shipyard, in common with most others, to extend the holiday period to almost one month.[15]

On 31 December 1926, A J Campbell retired, ending his eventful period as Works General Manager. His position was taken by the Engine Works Manager, Alexander Galbraith, a former superintendent engineer with the Cunard line.[16] In 1928 James Black was appointed Shipyard Manager with a five year contract at the handsome salary of £4,500.[17]

Despite the eventually successful introduction of the diesel engine to ship propulsion in the 1920s, the triple expansion reciprocating engine still enjoyed overwhelming popularity with ship owners. The reduced operating costs associated with the diesel encouraged engine builders to find ways of improving the efficiency of triple expansion machinery. Two developments which the Beardmore Company took up, are typical of the response made during the 1920s to the challenge of the diesel. In 1925, manufacturing rights for Caprotti valve gear were acquired offering an estimated saving in fuel of up to ten percent over ordinary valve gear. The first vessel to be fitted with this gear was the small steamer *Diamond* in 1928, followed in June of the same year by the much larger oil tanker, *Authority*. Although installed on these ships at Dalmuir, the Caprotti valve gear was made at Beardmore's Speedwell Works at Coatbridge. These works, which had been acquired in 1915, also made the small Beardmore two-stroke semi diesels for use in trawlers and other small craft. In 1929, the Speedwell Works were closed and manufacture was transferred to Dalmuir.

The other, and much more effective method of improving efficiency, was the exhaust steam turbine, the best example of which was that introduced by Dr Gustav Bauer and Dr Hans Wach known, appropriately enough, as the Bauer Wach Exhaust Turbine. In this system, steam from the low pressure cylinder is passed to the exhaust turbine which is coupled to the propeller shaft through double reduction gearing and a Vulcan hydraulic clutch. The extra power gained by this additional use of steam resulted in reduced fuel consumption of twenty percent. Beardmore acquired manufacturing rights in 1927 and from

A front view of a Beardmore-Caprotti marine steam engine.

then on a large number of merchant vessels had machinery of this type fitted at Dalmuir. The first ship was the Anchor Line's *Britannia* which demonstrated a twenty percent improvement in consumption on trials conducted in September 1928. In 1929 alone, no fewer than nineteen ships were fitted at Dalmuir with Bauer Wach gear.

The Beardmore diesel engine derived from the Italian Tosi engine was not neglected, despite the lack of demand, and continued development work at Dalmuir resulted in the first installation on board ship in the United Kingdom of a supercharged diesel. This engine, which was installed in the three Brazilian motorships building at Dalmuir, was nominally of 3,600 bhp although could achieve 4,000 bhp when supercharged. The first of the three motorships to run trials was the *Itapé* which achieved a speed of 14.8 knots on the measured mile in loaded condition which the Company claimed to be almost three knots over the contract speed.[18] Once again however, despite the apparent success of these engines, no further orders were received.

The Company's response to merchant ship propulsion in the late 1920s was comprehensive as the following summary of typical propulsion options prepared by A Galbraith, which essentially

On rousing the British Lion

The history of shipbuilding could be written from the annals of the Clyde. To-day, the Clyde shipyards and engineering shops are not working to capacity, not because of any question of deterioration in workmanship but as the outcome of the hundred and one causes which have led up to the present depression.

All are trying to find a way out.
There is a muffled sound just now of a slogan to "Buy British Goods." That cry will need to increase in volume until it reverberates in the ears of every patriotic citizen. There are none so blind as those who won't see and none so deaf as those who will not hear.
But see and hear they must.
"Buy British Goods," is no empty sounding slogan. Its application to shipbuilding, steelmaking and engineering should be immediate.
The Beardmore Shipyards are second to none. Every conceivable aid to efficient and economical production is there. Beardmore make their own steel plates, castings and forgings. So complete is their organization, that one visit to their marine engineering shops would give the lie direct to any implication that British Shipyards are not in the forefront of engineering progress.

Purchase British Ships

Preferably — Beardmore, — there are none better.

WILLIAM BEARDMORE
AND COMPANY LIMITED
NAVAL CONSTRUCTION WORKS, DALMUIR, near GLASGOW.

Above and opposite. Two adverts from a series placed in the magazine Shipbuilding & Shipping Record by the Company in 1926 during the midst of a deep and growing financial crisis. The copywriter is unknown but it would be easy to detect the hand of Lord Invernairn in the forthright and patriotic sentiments expressed. 'Backs To The Wall' would prove to be more appropriate than he could have known.

point to the overwhelming efficiency of the diesel, indicate –

1   Saturated steam triple expansion reciprocating engine of 5,000 ihp. Consumption 58.3 tons of fuel per day.
2   As above but with Caprotti valve gear. Consumption 46.8 tons per day.
3   As in 2, but with Bauer Wach exhaust turbine. Consumption 39.3 tons per day.
4   Supercharged diesel or high speed solid injection diesel. Consumption 22.5 tons per day.[19]

Throughout the 1920s the financial position of the armaments companies continued to deteriorate as a result of the wholesale reduction in defence spending. Of the large concerns with shipbuilding

interests, the Coventry Ordnance Works had ceased trading as such in 1918. The condition of Armstrong Whitworth was so critical that a merger with Vickers was pushed through in 1927, creating Vickers Armstrong Ltd retaining the warship yards at Barrow and the Tyne. Vickers remained in a relatively healthy position and in 1926, well aware of the Beardmore Company's precarious finances, decided to terminate their shareholding by selling to Lady Invernairn for the sum of only £75,000.

The last half of the 1920s was the period of greatest hardship for Dalmuir. Difficulties had been apparent from 1921 onwards and deficits had been incurred every year since 1923. The inability to generate sufficient business in the new areas in which they had become involved, together with the general trade depression, had so weakened the Company that drastic action to stem the losses became urgent. It is not the intention of this narrative to recount the complex interplay of schemes, personalities and survival plans which proliferated in the reconstruction of the Company.[20] However, the last few years of the Naval Construction Works at Dalmuir cannot be told without reference to the sequence of events orchestrated from the boardroom at Parkhead and beyond.

In March 1927, the critical position of the Company decided the board that a Committee of Enquiry, drawn from persons outwith the Company, should be formed to investigate the financial structure of the business. The first public expression of difficulty was made at this time and the following press statement released. 'The serious and prolonged depression in the shipbuilding, steel making and engineering trades, culminating in practically the entire cessation of production during the recent period of the coal strike, has seriously affected the financial resources of this company. . .'[21]

An insight into the way in which the company perceived its difficulties was given at the launch of the Canadian Pacific passenger ship *Duchess of Atholl* at Dalmuir on 23 November 1927. On this occasion, the Duke of Montrose, (the Marquis of Graham became the Duke of Montrose in December 1925) made the following speech which was reported in the *Glasgow Herald* the next day.

'. . . Messrs Beardmore's like other large firms, have been passing through very difficult and anxious times and these difficulties have been increased by the general depression in trade and by industrial strife. But, like wise men, they were taking stock – they had set up a committee of specialists, and they were looking forward to receiving a prescription which would restore them to health and strength. These were days when ideas of co-operation were in the air and they might, all round, from the point of view of the individual, the family and the nation, begin to realise that if they wished to achieve success and prosperity, they would have to act together. Shipbuilders should take the hint. They had heard the other day of the combination of two large firms in England with a capital of £21 million. In view of such great combinations, were they in Scotland to continue to cut each others throats in order to get a share of the limited work that was going? If they did so, the future of shipbuilding on the Clyde pointed to ruin and loss. If however, they came together they could prevent a vast amount of waste and extravagance, they could pool their knowledge and experience, they could avoid duplication of staffs and buy their materials and supplies in bulk; they could allocate their work to the yards and shops most suitable for carrying it out, get rid of surplus slips and shops and economise in labour and other ways. I make this gesture and believe it has the full approval of the chairman and fellow directors. If the gesture is received with sympathy elsewhere, they could look forward to a bright future for shipbuilding on the Clyde'.

The reference to the Vickers Armstrong merger and the threat which it posed is plain. It is equally clear that the application of a similar 'prescription' held favour with the board as the way forward although with which firm or firms they hoped to merge activities, is unknown. Ironically, while the Committee of Enquiry set about their task, Dalmuir shipyard became relatively busy. The cruiser *Shropshire*, submarines *Orpheus* and *Olympus* and the *Duchess of Atholl* were all in course of construction or fitting-out. Further contracts had been taken including another sludge boat, *Salford City*, two tugs, *Havaco* and *Northgate Scot* for Chilean and British owners, and a 10,000 ton cargo vessel *Manunda*. Disappointingly, the latter vessel was to be fitted with a Harland & Wolff built Burmeister & Wain diesel engine from their Finnieston engine works on the Clyde rather than a Beardmore diesel.

Throughout 1928, the Engine Works at last began to bear the fruits of their investment in the

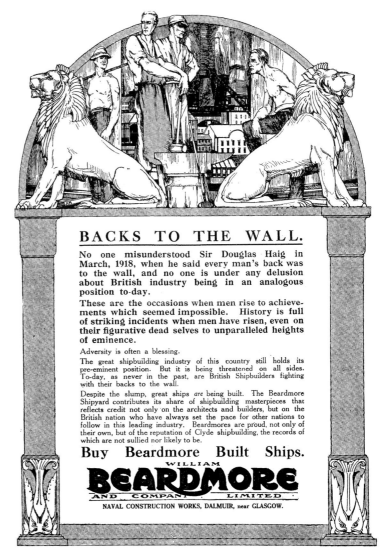

BACKS TO THE WALL.

No one misunderstood Sir Douglas Haig in March, 1918, when he said every man's back was to the wall, and no one is under any delusion about British industry being in an analogous position to-day.

These are the occasions when men rise to achievements which seemed impossible. History is full of striking incidents when men have risen, even on their figurative dead selves to unparalleled heights of eminence.

Adversity is often a blessing.

The great shipbuilding industry of this country still holds its pre-eminent position. But it is being threatened on all sides. To-day, as never in the past, are British Shipbuilders fighting with their backs to the wall.

Despite the slump, great ships *are* being built. The Beardmore Shipyard contributes its share of shipbuilding masterpieces that reflects credit not only on the architects and builders, but on the British nation who have always set the pace for other nations to follow in this leading industry. Beardmores are proud, not only of their own, but of the reputation of Clyde shipbuilding, the records of which are not sullied nor likely to be.

Buy   Beardmore   Built   Ships.

WILLIAM
BEARDMORE
AND   COMPANY   LIMITED
NAVAL CONSTRUCTION WORKS, DALMUIR, near GLASGOW.

Bauer Wach Turbine and Caprotti valve gear. In August the Clan Line contracted the firm to fit exhaust turbines to three of their vessels, *Clan McNair, Clan McNab* and *Clan McNeil*. The New Zealand Shipping Company's vessel *Tasmania* was similarly fitted while, in the same month, installation in the Anchor Line *Britannia* was completed with successful trials run in September.

In October 1928, the Committee of Enquiry made their recommendations public which were, for the time being, restricted to the balance sheet only. Cessation of some activities within Beardmore works was anticipated, the most likely being locomotive and aircraft at Dalmuir and cars at Paisley. The forge at Parkhead and the shipyard were not affected initially although should reorganisation of the latter prove necessary, the

East Yard would be dismantled to permit concentration at the Main Yard.[22] A new board was formed in which the status of both Lord Invernairn and the Duke of Montrose was reduced to that of non-executive director. This new board was then committed to 'sell or amalgamate any parts of the undertaking' as they saw fit.[23]

HOUSES OF STEEL

The Locomotive Works were also vulnerable and between the years 1922 and 1924 a total of only forty orders were received. From then until 1927, no locomotives were built at all and this presented the Company with the opportunity to commence the construction of steel houses in the otherwise redundant locomotive shops. The use of steel in house building had an advocate in the Duke of Atholl who found a willing partner in Lord Invernairn and at their behest, Atholl Steel Houses Limited was formed in 1924. The Housing Act of 1924, pushed through by John Wheatley MP, Minister of Health in the new Labour Government, provided the incentive for construction to begin as part of the answer to the national housing shortage. The first Beardmore

steel house was constructed in sections in the Locomotive Shops from plate made at Beardmore's Mossend works and inspected by the Duke of Atholl, John Wheatley and Vallentine Beardmore Stewart (Lord Invernairn's nephew and manager of the Parkhead works) on 1 September 1924.[24] This house, known as Atholl House, was a three bedroomed bungalow which was erected on Beardmore ground adjacent to the Works' main entrance. Large orders for Atholl Steel Houses of the semi-detached and 'four-in-a-block' type followed from the District Council who erected them in the Whitecrook district of Clydebank.[25]

Although floors, ceilings and roofs were of traditional construction, the main structure of the house comprised a steel frame clad on the outside with steel sheet of 11 and 12 guage. 573 steel houses were built between 1926 and 1928.

In 1927, the building of locomotives resumed alongside the manufacture of steel houses although the latter gradually lost favour as a result of pressure applied by the traditional brick and mortar house builders and the trade unions. Between 1927 and 1931, a further 168 locomotives were built at Dalmuir. 1928 was the best year with a total of 63.

In the absence of locomotive orders, Atholl steel houses were built in the locomotive shops during 1925/26. This example is in North Elgin Street, Whitecrook, Clydebank.

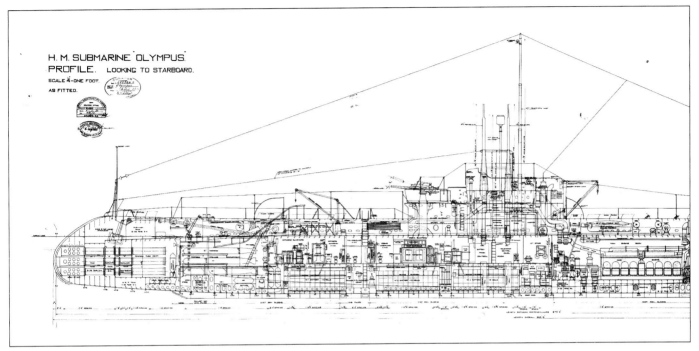

H. M. SUBMARINE 'OLYMPUS'.
PROFILE. LOOKING TO STARBOARD.
SCALE ¼-ONE FOOT.
AS FITTED.

Several of these orders were of interest including two electric and two diesel locomotives built for Indian Railways. During 1927, the Company fitted Caprotti valve gear to an LM&S 'Claughton' Class locomotive (No. 5908) to demonstrate the improved coal consumption possible in certain locomotive types with the use of this gear. Tested against a similar locomotive fitted with the standard Walschaerts gear, the Caprotti fitted engine demonstrated a significant saving in fuel.[26] Beardmore had sole manufacturing rights in the UK for Caprotti valve gear and many sets were manufactured at Dalmuir for fitting to existing locomotives as well as being incorporated into new construction at Dalmuir. In much the same way that Beardmore's recognition of the importance of diesels to marine propulsion went unrewarded, similar developments intended for locomotive traction made little progress. Beardmore diesels were fitted to several Canadian Pacific Railway's diesel electric locomotives and had, by mid 1927, been running for over 18 months with a total mileage of 600,000. Some sets ran for 110,000 miles without refit. Company interest was centred on the application of diesels to locomotives, motor trains and rail cars. The development work and manufacture of diesels was undertaken at Parkhead.[27]

By the end of 1928, the shipyard had, however, regained something of the appearance of the Naval Construction Works of former years with a considerable amount of Admiralty work in progress. In the fitting-out basin, the cruiser Shropshire and the submarines Orpheus and Olympus were fitting-out. More naval work appeared to be in the offing in February 1929 when the contract to build another submarine, Royalist, one of six submarines of the Rainbow Class, was won. Of the rest, three went to Vickers at Barrow, one to Chatham Dockyard and the last to Cammell Laird. In August, the Admiralty gave both Beardmore and Cammell Laird notice to suspend work on their submarine orders. At Dalmuir this resulted in the immediate laying off of 210 men who were working on the Royalist which had progressed well beyond the keel laying stage.[28] Efforts were made, following the cancellation of the Royalist, to find alternative government work for Dalmuir shipyard workers who had been laid-off and to afford them similar treatment to workers in the Royal Dockyards who had also suffered through loss of contract. These efforts were to no avail.[29] The suspension and eventual outright cancellation of these orders, along with two cruisers and a submarine depot ship all of which were building elsewhere, was forced by the newly elected Labour Government anxious to keep naval spending in check prior to the resumption of naval limitation talks at the London Naval Conference scheduled to begin in

A detail of a drawing, prepared at Dalmuir showing the forward section of the submarine Olympus. The drawing is dated 5 July 1930.

Drillers photographed under staging on 3 November 1927.

the following year. The question of the few naval orders that were to be placed had become a very vexed issue. The two cancelled cruisers, *Surrey* and *Northumberland*, had been the cause of great concern among private builders as the Admiralty had placed the orders with Portsmouth and Devonport Dockyards without putting them out to tender.[30]

In 1929, while the future of Dalmuir shipyard was in the balance, proposals for the rationalisation of the shipbuilding industry finally coalesced. In July, the Committee of Lloyds Register visited the Clyde and took the opportunity to discuss the difficulties the industry was facing with leading shipbuilders. Against statistics which showed that on average over the past five years, only 240 out of a total of 650 available berths in the United Kingdom were occupied, the following remarks were made —

'. . . this question must be seriously faced in order to ensure that when a genuine revival of trade takes place, the industry is not robbed of its proper share of prosperity by reason of any excess of facilities beyond that could be reasonably required to deal with any marked demand likely to arise . . . At present it is almost impossible to build except at a loss. The only way in which matters can be improved within the shipbuilding industry as a whole is for those interested to come to some arrangement by which redundant yards could be got rid of'.[31]

During the same month, the Bank of England agreed to offer financial assistance to the Beardmore Company in the belief that the retention of only the Parkhead works represented the best chance of survival for the firm. A further condition of this offer was that Lord Invernairn would resign from the board and cease to take any further part in the day to day running of the business. In his place a new chairman was found. The appointee was H A Reincke, an engineering graduate of Glasgow University who had previously been a director of the Coventry Ordnance Works. For Lord Invernairn, it must have come as a considerable blow to lose control of the Company which he had painstakingly built-up over the past few decades and even worse, to witness its dismantling despite the obvious need for restructuring.

The desire to rationalise the shipbuilding industry finally took definite shape with the incorporation of National Shipbuilders Security Limited in 1929. This company was brought into being, under the chairmanship of Sir James Lithgow, the lower Clyde shipbuilder, by the collective efforts of shipbuilders in the UK with the clear aim of reducing surplus building capacity the existence of which, it was argued, threatened more profitable yards. Agreement on the sale of Dalmuir shipyard for the sum of £200,000 to National Shipbuilders Security Limited was reached in March 1930, although no public statement was made for a further six months.

While these events were in train, the shipyard was working on what had now become the last contracts. In early 1930, the Glasgow firm of naval architects G L Watson placed orders for two large motor yachts the *Virginia* and the *Romany Rye*. The former, of 712 tons was launched in March while the latter, of 190 tons was launched in April. Two 9,000 ton cargo vessels *Daldorch* and *Dalhanna*, for J Campbell & Sons of Glasgow, were laid down in March. The following month saw the last ship order to be booked at Dalmuir, the twin screw supply ship *Pole Star* for the Northern Lighthouse Commission. On 15 March 1930, the new chairman H A Reincke went to Dalmuir for the launch of the motor yacht *Virginia* and made a rather inappropriate speech given that the shipyard had already been sold. Predicting greater activity at Dalmuir and Parkhead he said that, 'they (the Company) would look after their future and defend their name. No stone would be left unturned to contribute their share to the reconditioning of their great basic industry; they would see that the contribution of their company was a live and vigorous organisation worthy of its past achievements'.[32] It is not known what those assembled at the shipyard made of these comments for, if they had known of the shipyard's forthcoming closure they would surely have found them curiously contradictory. Although the shipyard had been sold, the Engine Works had been retained and initially it seemed as if a more favourable trading position could be achieved in the fitting of Bauer Wach exhaust turbines. Throughout 1929, no fewer than nineteen vessels had been taken in hand for the installation of this gear and largely as a result of this, a small profit of £30,000 was recorded for that year.

In May 1930, the cargo vessel *Carron* was completely overhauled for the Carron Company of Falkirk; the submarines *Olympus* and *Orpheus* commenced trials in June and the *Dalhanna* was launched on the 26th followed two months later by her sister the *Daldorch* on 27 August. The only ship remaining in the yard was the *Pole Star*. Announcement of closure was made public on 11 September 1930. The statement issued by the Company read,

'The Directors of Messrs William Beardmore and Company Limited, announce that they have disposed of the Company's shipbuilding yard at Dalmuir to National Shipbuilders Security Limited.

This step has been taken in view of the post-war curtailment of warship work and the absence of an adequate volume of the high-class mercantile work for which the yard was suitable, and in order to permit a concentration of the Company's resources on the development of the marine and general engineering works at Dalmuir, at their forge and steel works at Parkhead, and on the other branches elsewhere of the heavy industries in which they still hold a leading position among British firms'.

Closure, which did not take effect until the departure of the *Pole Star* at the end of the year, was accepted both within the yard and in the surrounding district with resigned reluctance although to some it seemed senseless to close such a well equipped and located yard.

Rumours of closure and talk of a 'displacement of labour' had been rife for some time, fuelled by the low level of employment in the yard which had been steadily reduced throughout the year until only 500 remained. The depression had put many people on the streets and by 1930, unemployment was accelerating beyond the two million mark.

The worst effects of closure on the Clydebank district had been alleviated to some extent by the placing of the order at John Brown's for the *Queen Mary*. This ship was so large that many Beardmore men from various trades were taken on. In December 1931 the suspension of this ship, then known only by her yard number '534', caused much more consternation locally than the closure of Dalmuir shipyard as it meant a complete stoppage, albeit temporary, of shipbuilding work in the district.

In addition to Dalmuir, four other shipyards on Clydeside were bought over and closed by National Shipbuilders Security Limited[33] and this period marked the first serious contraction of the shipbuilding industry on the Clyde. Nevertheless with thirty shipyards still in business, the Clyde continued as the premier shipbuilding river in the United Kingdom. In England the most significant closure effected by National Shipbuilders Security Ltd, was Palmers yard at Jarrow in 1933. Like Beardmore, this yard was closely identified with warship construction. The resulting hardship imposed on that district manifested itself in the Jarrow Crusade to London.

Significant reductions in shipbuilding capacity were effected by National Shipbuilders Security.

The men and woman of the brass finishing shop on 7 December 1927.

By October 1933, 116 berths had been dismantled by them and a further 43 were dismantled voluntarily by shipyard owners. The combined figure represented a reduction in UK capacity of 23%.[34]

The only recorded protest against the closure of Dalmuir shipyard occurred on the night of 27 October 1930, when Old Kilpatrick Parish Council, of which Dalmuir and Clydebank were sub-districts, agreed to forward copies of a unanimous resolution to the Prime Minister and Secretary of State for Scotland protesting against the 'destroying and laying to waste of the district by the demolition and removal of Dalmuir and Old Kilpatrick shipyards'. One JP said the removal of the Beardmore yard would be a calamity to Clydebank and district resulting in starvation and untold misery for the shipbuilding community as a whole.[35]

Although Lord Invernairn appears to have remained silent, in public at least, over the demise of his great naval shipbuilding yard, the Duke of Montrose, writing from Brodick Castle in Arran, was probably speaking for him as much as for himself when the following letter to the *Glasgow Herald* was printed on 13 September 1930:

'Sir, those of us who were associated with William Beardmore and Company in years gone past will appreciate the kindly remarks relative to the work of this firm made in your leading article in the issue of the 11th, but I think a word of sympathy should be added for the former chairman, Lord Invernairn, to whose vision, audacity and enterprise the growth and development of this wonderful manufacturing concern was almost entirely due. Throughout a quarter of a century, I had intimate and close personal relationships with him and I know the welfare of the firm, which includes the welfare of all its employees, was never far from his mind; and he was constantly thinking in what way his great organisation would take a leading part in the prosperity of the Clyde and the trade of the country. Hence it was that William Beardmore and Company 'dashed in' and took a lead in ordnance manufacture, submarine building, aircraft manufacture, and the making of railway plant, motors and steel houses etc. Indeed, anything that was up-to-date and was likely to be useful and promised employment for the people found a sympathetic and courageous supporter in Lord Invernairn. And now all of this enterprise is to be cut short if not wholly demolished and a life's work will be no more. Surely a bitter if unavoidable tragedy, and one which cannot be otherwise than a tremendous shock to the stoutest heart. It must not be thought for a moment that the late chairman did not see what was coming and failed to consider a remedy. He did observe the trend of conditions most acutely; and so it was on the occasion of the launch of the CPR liner Duchess of Atholl in 1927, he asked me to refer in my speech to the number of empty berths and redundant slipways on the river and to say that there was only one remedy, and that was that Clyde shipbuilders should come together and arrange to scrap all superfluous berths and close certain yards, and then get the remaining yards to specialise for the classes of tonnage best suited to their layout, and so far as possible, co-operatively perform and carry the necessary drawing office and other overhead expenditure. A few days later my remarks were alluded to by the chairman of one of the leading yards, and we were told that we did not know what we were talking about, as the glory of Clyde shipbuilders was their individuality and their freedom. And now it has come to this rather cynical tragedy that the firm which first saw the 'writing on the wall' is the first to suffer; but if in the sunset of William Beardmore and Company a lesson should be taken to heart by other great manufacturing concerns on the Clyde there may be some hope of saving industry on the river; otherwise I fear the trek of business to the south will become more rapid and dangerous. The departure of shipbuilding followed by steel-making would be a catastrophe too terrible to contemplate for the citizens of Glasgow'

This letter solicited a short reply from H A Reincke which was printed in the *Glasgow Herald* on 24 September.

'Sir, . . . I do not agree with the Duke of Montrose, although I respect the sentiments which lay behind his letter. But I think he will admit himself on reflection that the constructive work of Lord Invernairn can never be undone, and least of all by the reconditioning of William Beardmore and Company Limited in such a way that it may continue to be a live constructive and creative force in fighting to maintain the old traditions of one of Scotland's greatest industries'.

The departure of the lighthouse tender *Pole Star* on 5 January 1931 brought the shipbuilding activities of William Beardmore's Naval

Construction Works to a close. The remaining workforce was paid off and plans were immediately put in hand for the sale of plant and equipment. This function was carried out by Shirlaw Allan and Company, auctioneers of Hamilton, who then, as in years to come, presided over the dismantling and sale of much of the industry on Clydeside. The sale of the shipyard was organised into three portions the first of which lasted over eight days in February and March 1931. The second portion was in August while the third and last portion, which lasted over four days, ended on 15 April 1932. The catalogue for this last portion alone ran to almost 100 pages and contained no less than 1,751 lots ranging from the frying pans in the kitchen at the General Office to the Toplis luffing cranes in the East Yard.[36] In the dismantling of this shipyard as in its construction less than thirty years before, the statistics were impressive. In this manner, the shipyard was picked clean of its contents leaving only empty buildings and the giant shipbuilding gantry to stand over silent berths as a solitary monument to past achievements. In 1933, the gantry was sold as scrap and pulled down.

The Locomotive Works were also closed in 1930, it being estimated that up to £1,000 was lost on every locomotive built.[37] Diesel engines for railway traction continued to be made at Parkhead. However, a degree of optimism prevailed in the operation of the Engine Works after 1930 and Bauer Wach and Caprotti installations continued to be fitted to merchant ships. Between 1930 and 1934, warship turbine machinery contracts were won for the destroyer *Duncan*, the cruisers *Amphion* and *Apollo*, and the minesweeper *Speedwell*. Orders of this size took up only a small fraction of the plant at Dalmuir which needed a turnover of £300,000 to break even. With the continuation of an unsatisfactory trading position, the Engine Works were purchased late in 1934 by National Shipbuilders Security Ltd following a period in which the Company agreed to load its tenders to make them uncompetitive.[38] In February 1934, a proposal that Fairfield should acquire Dalmuir engine works was abandoned.[39]

Conditions of sale were similar to those imposed on the sale of the shipyard four years earlier and included the following manufacturing restrictions for the re-employment of the works,

(that) 1, main propelling machinery for use in

either naval or merchant ships, British or foreign (and) 2, boilers condensers and thrust blocks for use in such ships, was prohibited for a period of forty years from and after the 15th August 1934. The building of new ships and new shipbuilding work and ship repairing was prohibited for a period of twenty two years from the same date. [40]

THE RE-EMPLOYMENT OF DALMUIR SHIPYARD

The Beardmore Company had very little presence in the Dalmuir works from 1934 onwards although a small area was used by Beardmore Diesels Ltd. Proper re-employment of the former Engine and Locomotive Works did not take place until January 1939 when they were acquired by the Secretary of State for War for £210,000.[41] An armour plate scheme was installed in the shops for the production of tank armour. William Beardmore's legacy of extremely large shops made them eminently suitable for the task. The Beardmore Company, now centred solely on Parkhead, was asked to manage this facility throughout the war years. The entire area to the west of the fitting-out basin was designated a Royal Ordnance Factory and a considerable amount of new facilities and buildings was added during the war. The small shops and sheds between the Engine Shop and the fitting-out basin, including the submarine building sheds, were demolished to make way for new machine shops. In its final configuration, Dalmuir ROF comprised a West Shop (the original Engine and Boiler Shop and easily the biggest in the works), a North Shop (the former Locomotive Works), and a new East and South Shop.

During the war, this factory was also used for the production of medium calibre guns. The fitting-out basin was used by John Brown to complete eleven vessels throughout the war period. In 1951, the works were converted for the manufacture of armoured fighting vehicles which continued to be made there until 1957 when the Ministry of Supply announced the transfer of the works to Babcock & Wilcox. The lease was for 15 years with an option to break after five and a condition that the Admiralty retain right of access to the west side of the fitting out basin.[42] Babcock commenced the manufacture of cranes, pressure vessels and other complex heavy engineering products in 1959. A booklet produced by Babcock on taking over the works described the West Shop as one of the finest heavy engineering shops in

Great Britain. By 1969, Babcock had ceased to manufacture many of the products for which Dalmuir had been acquired and the site was disposed of. The buildings were stripped and demolished from 1971 to 1973. The 150 ton hammerhead crane which latterly had been down rated to 80 tons capacity was pulled over and cut up for scrap in April 1972.

The land to the east of the fitting-out basin formerly the shipyard, was divided among three main users. Arnott Young, metal merchants and shipbreakers, briefly occupied the East Yard before the GPO acquired the site and used the declivity of the berths to haul vessels up for breaking. In 1938 the East Yard was purchased by the GPO for conversion to a submarine cable ship base. The four building berths were excavated to form a basin where cable ships could be moored. The Platers Shed was given brick walls although remains externally the same building opened by Sir William Beardmore in 1921 .

The area to the immediate east of the fitting-out basin was occupied by Arnott Young, who, ironically, performed the task of breaking several of the ships built in the same yard. The first vessel to arrive at Dalmuir for breaking was the *City of Chester* on 1 January 1934. Indeed, the connection with battleships remained, as several British battleships including the *King George V* and the *Queen Elizabeth* were broken-up there. During the war, some of the original buildings in this section of the yard were destroyed during the Clydebank Blitz including the general office and joiners shop. Many of the others survived until the late 1980s and were used for storing scrap. The remaining centre section of the shipyard, including the main platers shed and aviation sheds, was acquired by Turners Asbestos Cement Company Ltd in 1938 who manufactured asbestos sheet material there until 1971. Asbestos and other waste was used to level-off the ground formerly occupied by the main shipbuilding berths and this later led to a great deal of activity to free the land from any asbestos contamination. All buildings on the shipyard site were cleared by 1987 and the filling in of the fitting-out basin was completed by 1989 marking the undoing of yet another piece of industrialisation on the River Clyde. In 1992, apart from the East Yard Platers Shed, power station and time office, not a single trace of the buildings comprising William Beardmore's great Naval Construction Works remain.

With her paint work heavily rust-streaked, the Empress of France, *returns to Dalmuir for demolition in November 1934.*

CONCLUSION

Despite building a first class shipbuilding yard at the right time in the right place, William Beardmore's Naval Construction Works was a loss maker in 15 out of 25 years. There are several reasons for this. In general terms, shipbuilding in Britain was in relative decline. Comparison between the years 1913 and 1930 show that, while output from Clydeside remained the same at about 33% of the UK total, the UK slipped from 53% to 45% of the world total.

However, this was of marginal significance overall and one must look to the shipyard itself to find the reasons for poor performance. Simply, the enormous cost of Dalmuir placed a great financial burden on the company which gave the yard very high operating costs and made it uncompetitive.

The pattern of orders at Napier's Govan yard, even making allowance for growth, did not warrant a yard as large as Dalmuir. Justification for Dalmuir could only have been made on the expectation of winning contracts because of the excellence of plant and facilities. The most cautious move for Beardmore would have been the upgrading of facilities at Govan, possibly creating one or two large berths and the acquisition of the adjacent yards as Harland & Wolff did later.

In comparison with Vickers and Armstrong, it is clear that Beardmore never succeeded in developing a critical relationship with the Admiralty in the way that the former had. Both Vickers and Armstrong enjoyed close links with the Admiralty not simply on a contractual basis but also in the important areas of warship and ordnance design, research and development. By the turn of the century, Vickers and Armstrong were major designers and builders of warships for foreign governments. This naturally gave rise to a degree of cross fertilisation in the design process between themselves and the Royal Corps of Naval Constructors who were responsible for the design of most British warships. The development of new designs for overseas by Vickers and Armstrong would almost certainly have subjected them to discrete evaluation by the Admiralty and this, together with the interchange of personnel which took place between them at a senior level, undoubtedly acted in the best interests of the Royal Navy and the country as a whole. The Beardmore Company, although to some extent styled as an ideas lead company in philosophy, never quite achieved that crucial position with the Admiralty.

In this, Beardmore was no different from most other Clydeside yards like Brown or Fairfield the exception being Yarrow who did make original contributions to the design of destroyers and their predecessors the torpedo boats. In many of the developments which presented themselves as a challenge to British armaments firms, like submarines, airships and aircraft, Beardmore

followed the lead of others, usually Vickers. This is not to suggest that Beardmore would not have taken the initiative if the opportunity had been there, for if nothing else, ample signals were made clearly indicating willingness to become involved in new ideas. The 1912 proposals for a hydroplane carrier were probably the closest the company came to being recognised as something more than a builder of fine ships.

When the depression threatened the armaments companies, it would have been unthinkable for Vickers or even the much less financially secure Armstrong to close by virtue of their central position in the defence of this country. In the case of Armstrong, great efforts were made to ensure that this did not happen although it meant the surrendering of Armstrong's autonomy in a merger with Vickers.

Even in acknowledging the highly significant role the Beardmore company played in the Great War and the unique contribution of the Dalmuir works in particular, they remained eager and capable builders among many.

In the widest sense contraction of naval capacity was entirely understandable. The postwar balance of power had shifted, reducing British naval power firstly from the Two Power Standard to that of outright superiority, and finally to first equal with the United States. The Washington Conference severely curtailed the need for new warships and left the naval yards in a precarious position. In simple numerical terms, this meant that after 1922 warship construction in Britain on the scale of the prewar naval race was over for the foreseeable future.

Although Dalmuir was built primarily to construct naval vessels as the logical extension of existing armaments and armour capacity at Parkhead, a plentiful demand for merchant ships would have been an acceptable alternative. This did not happen in sufficient volume to make the yard profitable. No lasting links with shipping lines were forged although the desirability of this was recognised and several attempts were made. When such links could well have been vital during the 1920s Beardmore had none and the contracts booked were few and unprofitable. This unenviable position compounded with the prolonged downturn in trade soon turned this very large yard into a loss maker of similar proportions, the propensity for which had been

amply demonstrated before the war in similar circumstances. A modestly equipped establishment with correspondingly reduced overheads and costs, might well have appeared a a sustainable asset rather than a liability when the pressure to rationalise the Company's activities grew – for ultimately the crown of financial success was not bestowed on William Beardmore and Company Limited.

In many ways the aviation activities of the Company remain the most intriguing. Despite the wealth of engineering expertise on Clydeside Beardmore was the only company taking a significant role in the design and development of aircraft and airships in what was clearly an area of great potential. In a purely Scottish context it must have seemed, for a time at least, that another great industry was in the making.

The poor financial performance resulting in the complete lack of reserves within the exhausted Beardmore company removed the possibility of survival and any temptation on the part of Lord Invernairn to impede the process of rationalisation – which one feels instinctively he would have done – was halted by his removal from the board.

He remains one of the most remarkable figures in British industrial history having succeeded through sheer determination, far-sightedness and enthusiasm for things mechanical in creating a major industrial complex centred on Clydeside employing 42,500 persons at its peak.

Overtaken by events, Lord Invernairn retired to his remote highland residence overlooking Loch Ness where he died on 9 April 1936 at the age of 80.

The Naval Construction Works were subdivided into four main blocks and sold off. This 1930s view of the main entrance and power station on Beardmore Street shows a sign fixed to the wall which reads Dalmuir Trading Estate.

A 1939 view of the area between the engine works and fitting-out basin being rebuilt as large shops for the Royal Ordnance Factory. This work necessitated the demolition of the West Yard and the filling-in of the shipbuilding berths as well as the former Clyde Trust slipways.

1. Ship List

Dimensions are in Imperial units. Length given is overall unless otherwise stated. Tonnage given is deep displacement for warships and gross for others. Dates are given where known. c = date of commissioning. t = date of trials. t. exp = triple expansion, q. exp = quadruple expansion, g = geared, Subsequent ship names in italics. The yard numbers are carried on from Robert Napiers Govan shipyard.

Yard No	Name	Owner Type	Laid Down Launched Completed	Principal Dimensions, Machinery, Armament	Fate
484	**Agamemnon**	Admiralty. Battleship, Lord Nelson Class	15/5/05 23/6/06 -/10/08	443.5 x 79.5 x 26 17,683t deep. 16,750 ihp 18 k. t. exp 4x12in 10x9.2in.	Sold for breaking Cashmore, Newport Mon. 24/1/27
485	**Zaza**	Wm Beardmore. Steam Yacht	— 5/7/05 -/9/05	190 x 24.1 x 13.9 423t t. exp. 650ihp	Broken-up Pollock Brown & Co Southampton 6/52
488	**Quillota** *Chile* 1923	Pacific Steam Navigation Co. Passenger Cargo	— 18/12/06 14/2/07	361.4bp x 46.2 x 22.2 3,673t t. exp 12k 4000ihp	Out of service 1931
489	**Quilpué** *Gascoyne*	"	— 28/3/07 9/5/07	" 3669t	Out of service 1931
490	**Huanchaco** *Frank Sutton* 1925 *Bore VIII*	" Cargo	— 15/6/07 -/8/07	390.6bp x 50.2 x 25.7 4524t 3500ihp	Broken-up 1939
491	**Junin** *Cambrian Idylle* 1925 *Petsamo*	"	— 22/8/07 -/9/07	" 4536t	
492	**Orcoma**	" Passenger	— 2/4/08 3/8/08	530 x 62.2 11,533t quad. exp. 12,000ihp 17k 1,150 passengers	Arrived for breaking Hughes Bolckow, Blyth 28/6/33
495	**Gloucester**	Admiralty. Cruiser, Bristol Class	15/4/09 28/10/09 -/9/10	453 x 47 x 15.5 5,300t turbines 22,000shp 25k. 2x6in 10x4in	Sold for breaking Ward. Arrived Portishead 7/22
496	**Pharos** *Avontoun* 1955	Northern Lighthouse Commission Tender	— 30/10/09 10/12/09	206.4bp x 31.2 x 15 921t t. exp 1500ihp	Arrived for breaking Shipbreaking Ind. Charlestown, Fife 3/9/55
497	**Shieldhall** *Shieldhall II*	Glasgow Corporation. Sludge Carrier	— 12/3/10 16/4/10t	260.8bp x 42.1 x 15 1,375t t. exp	Sold for breaking Smith & Houston, Port Glasgow 18/10/55
498	**Falmouth**	Admiralty. Cruiser, Weymouth Class	21/2/10 20/9/10 5/9/11c	453 x 48.5 x 15.5 5,800t turbines 22,000shp 25k 8x6in 4x3pdr.	Sunk North Sea by U63 19/8/16 & U52 20/8/16
500	**Conqueror**	Admiralty. Battleship, Orion Class	5/4/10 1/5/11 -/11/12	581 x 88.5 x 25 25,870t turbines 27,000shp 21k 10x13.5in 16x4in	Sold for breaking Upnor Shipbreaking Co Ltd 19/12/22
501	**Goshawk**	Admiralty. Destroyer, Acheron Class	30/1/11 18/10/11 30/5/12	246 x 25.7 x 9 990t turbines 13,500shp 27k 2x4in 2x12pdr 2x21inTT	Sold for breaking Rees, Llanelly 4/11/21

Yard No	Name	Owner Type	Laid Down Launched Completed	Principal Dimensions, Machinery, Armament	Fate
503	**Dublin**	Admiralty. Cruiser, Chatham Class	4/4/11 30/4/12 -/5/13	458 x 49 x 16 6,000t turbines 25,000shp 25.5k 8x6in 4x3pdr 2x21TT	Sold for breaking King, Troon 30/7/26 stranded
505	**Warilda**	Adelaide Steamship Company. Passenger Cargo	— 5/12/11 9/7/12t	429 x 56.7 7,785t q. exp 8500ihp 11k	Torpedoed off Isle of Wight 3/8/18
506	**Wandilla** *Fort St George* 1920 *Cesarea* 1935, *Arno* 1938	"	— 25/5/12 6/10/12t	"	Sunk off Tobruk by RAF torpedo bomber 1942
507	**Willochra** *Fort Victoria* 1919	"	— 14/8/12 7/2/13t	" 7.784t	Sunk in collision 28/12/29 off Ambrose light vessel New York
509	**Alsatian** *Empress of France* 1919	Allan Line. Passenger	— 22/3/13 16/12/13t	600 x 72.2 18,485t turbines 21,400shp 20k 1,745 passengers 500 crew	Arrived for breaking Arnott Young 24/11/34 Dalmuir
510	**Benbow**	Admiralty. Battleship, Iron Duke Class	30/5/12 12/11/13 7/10/14	622.75 x 90 x 29.5 29,560t turbines 29,000shp 21k 10x13.5 12x6in	Arrived for breaking Metal Industries, Rosyth 5/4/31
511	**Llewellyn** (ex Picton)	Admiralty. Destroyer, Laforey Class	14/12/12 30/10/13 31/3/14	268.9 x 27.7 x 10.5 1,300t turbines 24,500shp 29k 3x4in 4x21inTT	Sold for breaking J Smith, Poole 10/3/22
512	**Lennox** (ex Portia)	"	18/11/12 17/3/14 22/5/14t	"	Sold for breaking Barking Shipbreaking Co 26/10/21
513	**Galatea**	Admiralty. Light Cruiser, Arethusa Class	9/1/13 14/5/14 5/12/14t	436 x 39 x 13.5 4,400t turbines 40,000shp 28.5k 2x6in 6x4in 1x3pdr	Sold for breaking Multilocular Shipbuilding Co. Stranraer 25/10/21
514	**Inconstant**	"	3/4/13 6/7/14 -/1/15	"	Sold for breaking Cashmore 9/6/22 Newport Mon.
515	**Royalist**	"	3/6/13 14/1/15 25/3/15t	"	Sold for breaking Cashmore 24/8/22 Newport Mon
516	**Ramillies**	Admiralty. Battleship Royal Sovereign Class	12/11/13 12/10/16 -/10/17	620.5 x 101.5 x 33.5 33,570t turbines 40,000shp 21k 8x15in 14x6in 2x3in	Sold for breaking Arnott Young Cairnryan 20/2/48 arrived 23/4/48. Hulk to Troon 10/49
518	**Nearchus**	Royal Indian Marine. light house tender	-/10/13 15/11/14 7/12/14	180.1bp x 28.9 x 10.8 925t g. turbines 550 shp 11k	

Yard No	Name	Owner Type	Laid Down Launched Completed	Principal Dimensions, Machinery, Armament	Fate
519	**Argus**	Admiralty. Aircraft Carrier	-/6/14 2/12/17 -/9/18	566 x 68 x 21 14,550t turbines 20,000shp 20k 20 aircraft 6x4in	Arrived for breaking Ward, Inverkeithing 12/12/46
520	**E25**	Admiralty. Submarine, E Class	-/11/14 23/8/15 2/10/15c	182.5 x 15.1 x 12.5 807t diesel/electric 1,600hp/ 840hp 15/9k 5x18inTT	Sold for breaking Petersen & Albeck 14/12/21
521	**E26**	"	-/11/14 11/11/15 20/12/15c	"	Sunk North Sea 6/7/16
522	**Clive**	Royal Indian Marine. Sloop	— 10/12/19 20/4/20t	262.3 x 38.5 x 13.8 2,100t g. turbines 1,700shp 14.5k 2x4in 2x2pdr	Sale List 1947
523	**Lawrence**	"	— 30/7/19 27/12/19	241.5 x 34 x 12 1,412t g. turbines 1,900shp 15k 2x4in 1x2pdr	Sale List 1947
526	**Lassoo** (ex Magic)	Admiralty. Destroyer, War emergency repeat L Class	24/1/15 24/8/15 11/10/15	268.9 x 27.7 x 10.5 1,300t turbines 24,500shp 29k 3x4in 4x21inTT	Sunk (mined) North Sea 13/8/16
527	**Lochinvar** (ex Malice)	"	9/1/15 9/10/15 1/12/15	"	Sold for breaking Hayes, Porthcawl 25/11/21
528	**E53**	Admiralty. Submarine, E Class	— -/-/16 8/3/16c	182.5 x 15.1 x 12.5 807t diesel/electric 1,600hp/ 840hp 15/9k 5x18inTT	Sold for breaking C A Beard 06/09/22
529	**E54**	"	— -/-/16 18/5/16c	"	Sold for breaking Petersen & Albeck 14/12/21
533	**X156 to X175** (20)	Admiralty. X Lighters, Landing Craft	ordered 2/15 8/15	105.5 x 21 x 3.5 160t diesel 60bhp some by Bolinders some by Beardmore	
537	**Pelican**	Admiralty. Destroyer Repeat M Class	25/6/15 18/3/16 1/4/16	273.5 x 26.75 x 8.5 1,250t turbines 25,000shp 34k 3x4in 1x2pdr 4x21inTT	Sold for breaking Ward, Preston 9/5/21 Arrived 11/5/24
538	**Pellew**	"	28/6/15 18/5/16 30/6/16	"	Sold for breaking Ward, Briton Ferry 9/5/21 Arrived 1/23
546	**P50** (ex Irrawaddy)	Royal Indian Marine. 'Tigris' Paddle Transport	1916/17 — —	338t t. exp 1200ihp 15k 2 machine guns	

ard No	Name	Owner Type Completed	Laid Down Launched	Principal Dimensions, Machinery, Armament	Fate
47	P51 (ex Sladen)	Royal Indian Marine. 'Tigris' Paddle Transport	1916/17 — —	270t t. exp 1,200ihp 15k 2 machine guns	
49	Satyr	Admiralty. Destroyer, R Class	15/4/16 27/12/16 2/2/17	276 x 26.7 x 9 1,173t g. turbines 27,000shp 36k 3x4in 1x2pdr 4x21inTT	Sold for breaking Ward, Milford Haven 16/12/26
50	Sharpshooter	"	23/5/16 27/2/17 2/4/17	"	Sold for breaking Ward, Briton Ferry 24/4/27
51	Raleigh	Admiralty. Cruiser Cavendish Class	9/12/15 28/8/19 -/2/21	605 x 65 x 19.25 12,190t g. turbines 70,000shp 31k 7x7.5in 6x12pdr 4x3in	Ran aground, Labrador Constructive total loss 8/8/22
55	K16	Admiralty. Submarine, K Class	— 5/11/17 22/2/18c	330 x 26.5 x 17 2,566t g. turbines/elec motors 10,500shp/1,440hp 24/9k 10x18inTT 2x4in 1x3in	Arrived for breaking Alloa Shipbreaking Co Charlestown 16/9/24
56	Tancred	Admiralty. Destroyer, Repeat M Class	6/7/16 30/6/17 1/9/17	273.5 x 26.75 x 8.5 1,250t g. turbines 27,000shp 36k 3x4in 1x2pdr 4x21inTT	Sold for breaking Cashmore 17/5/28, Stranded Port Talbot and broken there
57	Tyrrhenia Lancastria 1924	Cunard Line. Passenger Ship	2/6/19 31/5/20 12/6/22	578 x 70.2 16,243t g. turbines 13,500shp 17k 1,785 passengers 320 crew	Bombed and sunk St Nazaire 17/16/40 3,000-5,000 lost
60	Ulster	Admiralty. Destroyer, Modified R Class	19/9/16 10/10/17 21/11/17	276 x 26.7 x 9 1,173 g. turbines 27,000shp 36k 3x4in 1x2pdr 4x21inTT	Sold for breaking Ward, Pembroke 21/4/28
61	L6	Admiralty. Submarine, L Class	— 14/1/18 10/7/18	231 x 23.5 x 13.25 1,074t diesel/elec. 2,400hp/1,600hp 17/10k 6x18TT 1x4in	Sold for breaking Cashmore 17/1/35 Newport Mon
63	Vancouver Vimy 1928	Admiralty. Destroyer, V Class	15/3/17 28/12/17 9/3/18	312 x 29.5 x 10.5 1,490t g. turbines 27,000shp 34k 4x4in 1x3in 4x21in TT	Handed over for breaking Metal Industries 4/3/47 bu 12/47
64	Vanessa	"	16/5/17 16/3/18 27/4/18	"	Handed over for breaking Metal Industries 4/3/47 Arrived 5/9/48
65	HP4	Admiralty. Hospital Paddle Ship	19/6/17 — —	225.5pp x 30 x 6.5 t. expansion 1,000ihp 12k	
66	HP5	"	"	"	

Yard No	Name	Owner Type	Laid Down Launched Completed	Principal Dimensions, Machinery, Armament	Fate
567	**HP6**	"	"	"	
568	**HP7**	"	20/8/17(L)	"	
570	**Vanity**	Admiralty. Destroyer, V Class	28/7/17 3/5/18 21/6/18	312 x 29.5 x 10.5 1,490t g. turbines 27,000shp 34k 4x4in 1x3in 4x21in TT	Handed over for breaki⬛ Brunton, Grangemouth 4/3/47
574	**B476 to B487**	War Office. Y Lighters (dumb barges)		2,700 tons in total	
580	**L69**	Admiralty. Submarine, L 50 Class	7/7/17 6/12/18 -/3/23	235 x 23.5 x 13.1 1,150t diesel/elec. 2,400/1,600hp 17/10.5k 6x21inTT 2x4in	Sold for breaking Arnott Young, Dalmuir 23/10/38 (at Rosyth)
581	**L70** (cancelled 26/11/18)	"		"	Hull sold for use by Leit⬛ Salvage Co as salvage camel LS3 1/3/20. Sol⬛ Ward Inverkeithing for breaking 13/12/38
584	**Cameronia** Empire Clyde 1953	Anchor Line. Passenger Ship	7/3/19 23/12/19 -/3/21	578 x 70.2 16,280t g. turbines 13,500shp 17k 1,785 passengers 320 crew	Arrived for breaking to Cashmore, Newport 22/10/57
589	**Tactician**	Admiralty. Destroyer, S Class	21/11/17 7/8/18 23/10/18	276 x 26.7 x 9 1,075t g. turbines 27,000shp 36k 3x4in 1x2pdr 4x21inTT	Arrived for breaking Metal Industries, Charlestown 5/2/31
590	**Tara**	"	21/11/17 12/10/18 9/12/18	"	Sold for breaking Rees, Llanelly 17/12/31
591	**Tasmania** (transferred to RAN 06/19)	"	18/12/17 22/11/18 29/1/19	"	Sold for breaking Penguins Ltd, Sydney 4/6/37
592	**Tattoo**	"	21/12/17 28/12/18 7/4/19	"	as above but 9/1/37
593	**H47**	Admiralty. Submarine, H Class	— 19/11/18 25/2/19	171.75 x 15.75 x 13.1 510t diesel/electric 480/620hp 11.5/10.5k	Sunk after collision with L12, 9/7/29
594	**H48**	"	— 31/3/19 23/6/19	"	Sold for breaking Rees, Llanelly 30/8/35
595	**H49**	"	— 15/07/19 25/10/19	"	Sunk off Dutch coast by German patrol vessels 27/10/40

ard No	Name	Owner Type	Laid Down Launched Completed	Principal Dimensions, Machinery, Armament	Fate
6	H50	"	— 25/10/19 3/2/20	"	Sold for breaking Troon 7/45
9	Vansittart	Admiralty. Destroyer, Modified W Class	1/7/18 17/4/19 20/10/19	312 x 29.5 x 10.5 1,508t g. turbines 27,000shp 34k 4x4.7in 1x3in 2x2 pdr 6x21inTT	Arrived for breaking Cashmore 5/5/46
0	Vantage Vimy (cancelled 09/18)	"	16/9/18	"	broken-up on berth
2	Daring (cancelled 26/11/18)	Admiralty. Light cruiser, Danae Class	ordered 3/18		broken-up on berth
3	Desperate (cancelled 26/11/18)	"	"	"	
4	Vashon (cancelled 12/18)	Admiralty. Destroyer, Modified W Class	ordered 4/18		"
5	Vengeful (cancelled 12/18)	"	"		"
6	L59 (cancelled)	Admiralty. Submarine, L 50 Class	ordered 4/18		"
1	Conte Rosso	Lloyd Sabaudo. Passenger liner	— 10/2/21 14/3/22t	588.2 x 74.1 18,017t g. turbines 22,000shp 20k 2,366 passengers 442 crew	Sunk by British sub Upholder off Syracuse 24/5/41 800 dead
2	Conte Verde Kotobuki Maru 1944	"	16/1/20 21/10/22 4/4/23t	592.3 x 74.1 18,017t g. turbines 22,000shp 20k 2,400passengers 440 crew	Sunk off Maizuru in American air raid 1944 Raised & b.u. by Mitsui 1951
3	Setter Lady Kildare Ulster Castle 1932	G&J Burns. Passenger/cargo	— 26/1/20 30/4/20t	245 bp x 34.1 x 15.6 1,217t t expansion.	Arrived Ward, Preston for breaking 8/6/50
5	Hannah E Reynolds Elizabeth Angela	Beardmore. (speculative) trawler	— 25/1/28 -/2/28	120.7 bp x 23.1 x 12.5 253t t. exp 84ihp (Coatbridge)	Sunk by German aircraft off Deal 13/8/40
6	Largs Bay	Commonwealth Government Line. Passenger Cargo	— 20/6/21 22/12/21t	552 x 68.2 13,851t g. turbines 9,000shp 15k 722 passengers 215 crew	Sold to Bisco 4/57 Broken up Ward, Barrow arrived 22/8/57

Yard No	Name	Owner Type	Laid Down Launched Completed	Principal Dimensions, Machinery, Armament	Fate
617	**Esperance Bay** _Arawa_ 1936	"	— 15/12/21 11/7/22t	552 x 68.2 13,851t g. turbines 9,000shp 15k 722 passengers 215 crew	Arrived for breaking Cashmore Newport 21/5/55
618	**Pinzon** _Havny_ 1951	MacAndrews Co Ltd. Cargo	— 15/11/21 14/1/22	249.8 x 38.2 x 15.7 1,367t B Tosi diesel 1,250hp 12k	Sold for breaking Belgium 1961
619	**Pizarro**	"	— 11/9/22 18/1/23t	"	Sunk off Gibraltar 31/1/41
621	**British Trader** _Flisvos_ 1953 _Manco Capac_ 1955	British Tanker Company. Oil tanker	— 8/7/21 2/11/21t	363.2 x 49.1 4,204t t. exp. 10k	
622	**British Merchant**	"	— 24/8/22 27/10/22t	440.7bp x 57.2 6,994t turbines	Arrived Hughs Bolckow, Blyth for breaking 16/8/49
623	**British Enterprise**	"	— 18/10/21 6/1/22t	363.2 x 49.1 4,204t t.exp. 10k	Arrived West of Scotland Shipbreaking, Troon for breaking 10/4/36
624	**British Industry** _Saint Jerome_ _Shapur_ 1929	"	— 14/1/22 6/4/22t	4,121t	oil hulk 4/39
625	**British Commerce**	"	— 26/5/22 22/8/22t	4,205t	Sold for breaking at Hendrik-ido-Ambacht 19/1/37
627	**G3** (design prefix)	Admiralty. Battlecruiser ordered 1/11/21 cancelled 13/2/22		856 x 106 x 35.7 53,909t g. turbines 160,000shp 32k 9x16in 16x6in 6x4.7in 40x2pdr 2x24.5TT	not laid down
628	**Henry Ward**	London CC. Sludge Carrier	-/2/23 14/8/23 18/9/23t	267 x 43.2 x 15.3 1,438t t. expansion	Sold for breaking Antwerp arrived 28/1/64
630	**Arcoona** _Arkaba_ 1929 _William Charlick iv_ 1954	Adelaide Steamship Co. Passenger cargo	— 6/3/24 10/5/24t	352 x 47.2 4,212t t. expansion 2300ihp 11k	Sold for breaking Hong Kong 13/2/59
631	**Allara** _Santelena_ 1952	"	— 29/5/24 10/7/24t	352 x 47.2 3,279t t. expansion 2300ihp 11k	Arrived for breaking Shipbreaking Industries Charlestown 22/12/53
633	**Carlota** _Island Spruce_ 1954	Anglo Saxon Petroleum Co. Oil Tanker	— 29/4/24 21/6/24t	305 bp x 50.2 x 15 2,696t t. expansion	Reduced to barge 1954

Yard No	Name	Owner Type	Laid Down Launched Completed	Principal Dimensions, Machinery, Armament	Fate
634	**Krisjanis Valdemars**	Government of Latvia. Icebreaker	— 9/6/25 25/9/25t	196.5bp x 55.7 x 22.1 2,800t t. expansion	Not listed after 1960
635	**Hebble**	LMS Railway. Cargo	— 7/7/24 2/9/24t	250 x 34.4 x 15.2 1,040t t. expansion 1,800ihp	Sold for breaking Rotterdam 1959
636	**Rye**	"	— 21/8/24 9/10/24	" 1,048t	Sunk by E-boat off Cromer 7/3/41
637	**Ulooloo** *Clyde Breeze* 1957 *Hankong* 1962	Adelaide Steamship Co. Cargo ship	— 10/10/24 18/11/24t	343.5 x 46.6 x 23 3,236t t. expansion	Sold for breaking Hong Kong arrived 29/6/62
638	**Conchita** *Island Hemlock* 1954	Anglo Saxon Petroleum Co. oil tanker	— 29/4/24 10/9/24t	305bp x 50.2 2,702t t. expansion	Reduced to barge 1954
640	**Conte Biancamano** *Hermitage* 1942 *Conte Biancamano* 1947	Lloyd Sabaudo Line. Passenger liner	-/6/24 23/4/25 7/11/25t	653 x 76.1 24,416t g. turbines 24,000shp 21k 1,750 passengers 500 crew	Arrived La Spezia for breaking 16/8/60
641	**Cassandra**	Anglo Saxon Petroleum Co. Oil tanker	— 18/11/24 -/12/24	305bp 50.2 2701t t. expansion (Coatbridge)	
642	**Chepita** *Island Fir* 1954	"	— 11/12/24 -/1/25	305bp x 50.2 2702t t. exp (Coatbridge)	Reduced to barge 1954
643	**John Perring**	London CC. Sludge Carrier	-/7/25 26/2/26 14/4/26	267 x 43.7 x 15.7 1,551t t. expansion (Coatbridge)	Sold for breaking Ward, Inverkeithing arrived 1/6/68
644	**Itapé**	Companhia Nacional de Navegaco Costiera. P/Cargo	— 2/6/27 2/11/27t	386 x 52 x 25 4,978t B Tosi supercharged diesel 4,000bhp 14k 270 passengers	Not listed after 1962
645	**Itaquicé**	"	— 14/9/27 31/1/28t	" 4969t	Sold for breaking Rio de Janiero 1950 after fire damage
646	**Itanagé**	"	— 28/10/27 18/4/28t	" 4966t	Not listed after 1965
647	**Shropshire** (transferred to RAN 1943)	Admiralty. Cruiser London Class	-/2/27 5/7/28 12/9/29	633 x 66 x 20.75 13,315t g. turbines 80,000shp 32k 8x8in 4x4in 4x3pdr 8x21inTT	Sold for breaking Arnott Young Dalmuir arr. 20/1 /55, Troon arr. 19/9/55

Yard Name No	Owner Type	Laid Down Launched Completed	Principal Dimensions, Machinery, Armament	Fate
648 **Duchess of Atholl**	Canadian Pacific Steamships. Passenger liner	— 23/11/27 -/6/28	601 x 75.1 20,119t g. turbines 21,180shp 19k 1,563 passengers 518 crew	Sunk off Ascension by U178 10/10/42
649 **Olympus**	Admiralty. Submarine, O Class	— 11/12/28 -/6/29	283.5 x 30 x 16 2,038t diesel/elec 4,520/1,390 hp 17.5/8k 8x21inTT 1x4in	Sunk off Malta after striking mine 8/5/42
650 **Orpheus**	"	— 26/2/29 26/6/29t	"	Sunk Mediterranean by Italian sub Turbine 27/6/40
651 **Manunda** *Hakone Maru* 1956	Adelaide Steamship Co. Passenger Cargo ship	— 27/11/28 16/4/29t	447.7 x 60.2 9,115t H&W diesel 10,000bhp 16k 300 passengers	Not listed after 1956
652 **Salford City**	Salford County Council Sludge Carrier	— 28/6/28 12/10/28t	246 x 38.1 x 15 1,179t t. expansion (Coatbridge)	Sold for breaking Mayer Newman & Co Fleetwood, arr. 24/6/76
653 **Havaco**	Cia. Habanera De Vapores & Lanchas. Tug	— 16/8/28 -9/28	84bp x 20.6 x 10 158t	not listed after 1940
655 **Northgate Scot** *St Denys* 1959	Falmouth Docks & Engineering Co. Tug	— 15/1/29 -/1/29	90.5bp x 25.1 x 12.1 174t t exp (Coatbridge) 790 ihp	Preserved Falmouth Maritime Museum Sold to French Museum 1991
656 **Royalist** cancelled 08/29	Admiralty. Submarine R Class		287.1 x 30 x 16 2,030t diesel/elec 4,640/1,670hp 17.5/8.8k 8x21in 1x4.7in	Broken-up on berth
658 **Romany Rye** *Henry Morgan* *Sheran* *Henry Morgan*	Sir Gervasse Beckett. Motor yacht	— 24/4/30 29/5/30t	111bp x 21 x 9.6 190t	Refitted 1984 USA with 2 MAN diesels. Still in service
660 **Virginia** *Liberian* 1957	Maj. Stephen Courtauld. Motor yacht	— 15/3/30 15/5/30t	209.5 x 29.8 x 13.9 712t Sulzer diesels. 2x600bhp 14k.	Modernised, re-engined 1965/66
661 **Dalhanna** *Lord O' Neil* 1946 *Johann Schulte* 1950	J M Campbell & Son. Cargo ship	-/3/30 26/6/30 29/8/30t	420.8 x 55 x 25 8,800dwt t exp B/W exhaust turbines 2750ihp 12k	Sold for scrapping Vigo Spain arr. 26/9/62
662 **Daldorch** *Lord Glentoran* 1945 *Kosmat* 1950	"	-/3/30 27/8/30 28/10/30	"	Not listed after 1971
663 **Pole Star** *May* 1961	Northern Lighthouse Commission. Lighthouse tender	— 4/11/30 -/12/30	204 x 31 x 15.2 1,275t t. expansion	Broken-up P&W McLellan Boness 8/64

NOTES
All the ships built at Dalmuir were fitted with engines built there with the following exceptions.
The engines for *Agamemnon* were built by Hawthorn Leslie.
"   "   *Manunda* were built by Harland & Wolff.
"   "   *British Merchant* were built by Metropolitan Vickers.
Casandra, Chepita, John Perring, Northgate Scot, Salford City, were fitted with engines built at Beardmore's Speedwell Works, Coatbridge.
A number of 'X' lighters (yard no. 533) were sold, converted to mercantile duties and given names.
The following is a list of such vessels originally built by Beardmore as 'X' lighters.
Ramble (ex *X161*); *Serabu* (ex *Beatrice Hope*); *Sherfield* (renamed *AHP* in 1963); *Swanage* (renamed *Mary Birch* in 1935)*;
Airston (ex *X169*); *Alpheus; Mardby* (renamed *Peter Robin* in 1951)*; *Stanley Baldwin* (ex *X167*) became *Laika* in 1947, *Elmo* in 1952, *Gutholz* in 1965.
*These vessels were still listed in 1989 and, together with tug *Northgate Scott* (*St Denys*) and the *Romany Rye* (*Henry Morgan*), are the only Beardmore built vessels known to be afloat.

Bauer Wach Exhaust Turbines (BWET) and other Machinery Contracts
1928: BWET for *Britannia, Tasmania*. Caprotti valve gear fitted to *Authority* and *Diamond*
1929: BWET for *Clan Macpherson, Jumna, Koomilya, Clan McNaughton, Clan McNab, Clan McNair, Gryfedale , Baradine,*
        Balranald, Ballarat, Bendigo, Barrabool, Barrwhin, Ardanbahn, Clan Macalister, Comorin plus one unnamed vessel. Total of
        32,860ihp.
1930: BWET for *Clan Murdoch, Clan Skene, Banffshire*.
1931: BWET for *Buteshire, Clan Murray, Clan Mackinlay, Clan Stuart and Hilary*. Total of 7,000ihp
1932: No Bauer Wach installations. Turbines for *HMS Duncan* 36,000shp. Triple expansion engines for *HMS Skylark* 400ihp.
1933: No main machinery constructed. Twelve Vulcan hydraulic clutches for Admiralty. Caprotti valve gear for four twin screw
        steamers and a quantity of general engine and boiler work for home and abroad.
1934: BWET for two vessels building at Cammell Laird totalling 2,100ihp

Miscellaneous work at Dalmuir
Atalanta – reconditioned 1919. Contract price £25,000.
Alsatian – reconditioned 1919. Contract price £279,091 includes profit of £38,056
The barque *Portugal* was fitted with Beardmore diesels at Dalmuir during 1921
Empress of France (ex *Alsatian*) – Reconditioned and conversion to oil burning; in yard for six months during 1924.
Contract price £84,600
California – overhauled 1926
Salvor – hull repairs 1929
Kia Ora – reconditioned February 1930
Tuscania – overhauled 1930
Carron – reconditioning 1930

Bauer Wach and Vulcan Clutch Contracts
These contracts received the prefix BW and VC
VC contracts numbered up to 6.
BW contracts had reached up to 40 by August 1937

A large number of small craft were fitted with 'Peck' type semi diesels.

Ships completed by Beardmore at Govan shipyard
The following ships were completed or built by Beardmore at Robert Napiers Govan shipyard between the years 1900 and 1905. *Talca, Highland Brigade, Industry, Berwick, Alnwick Castle, Berwick Castle, Atmah, Empire, Iolaire, Carnarvon, Dalmuir, Highland Laddie* and *Rathlin*.

2. Output (tonnage)
Beardmore and main competitors

Year	Beardmore	Fairfield	Brown	Armstrong	Vickers	UK Total
1901	17,390	28,565	49,800	39,597	26,700	1,799,088
1902	15,258	30,300	26,260	52,039	18,382	1,619,040
1903	10,700	39,053	55,152	48,740	42,912	1,404,019
1904	2,350	6,955	23,150	37,147	13,280	1,421,600
1905	6,250	37,835	20,606	67,652	41,500	1,824,750
1906	21,050	20,063	46,387	36,814	26,770	2,030,900
1907	14,500	48,020	35,392	74,228	4,882	1,847,200
1908	11,533	17,520	15,300	51,384	12,487	1,077,226
1909	6,000	27,688	10,154	15,964	60,200	1,203,496
1910	7,400	9,400	18,564	21,936	18,130	1,341,442
1911	31,400	40,107	65,613	74,128	49,960	2,088,658
1912	20,926	36,626	22,782	41,535	52,860	2,108,230
1913	44,435	33,200	82,722	99,333	64,700	2,311,960
1914	8,970	38,850	34,420	48,989	65,600	1,722,154**
1915	11,680	26,886	12,480	52,496	11,600	649,336**
1916	35,310	39,389	46,120	66,027	49,200	
1917	27,700	17,703	37,289	54,339	35,500	
1918	10,450	30,910	22,196	72,649	30,500	1,840,029
1919	33,520	13,997	65,050	43,250	33,500	1,927,281
1920	17,716	40,234	40,090	41,229	35,400	2,140,928
1921	60,179	24,860	44,920	98,390	64,320	1,596,272
1922	31,066	12,000	27,250	54,689	21,342	1,043,590
1923	1,438		11,355	18,893	2,183	685,147
1924	23,609	30,960	40,152	32,329	42,670	1,487,848
1925	25,212	33,080	24,300	64,424	47,100	1,195,487
1926	1,620	22,886	33,034	29,346	25,536	730,134
1927	36,434	27,080	22,150	66,726	22,439	1,314,380
1928	22,131	47,854	78,117	61,641	35,120	1,573,582
1929	1,714	25,212	45,007	44,070	35,100	1,623,430
1930	12,726	23,152	50,982	88,395	19,311	1,569,679

Until 1905 at Govan, thereafter at Dalmuir. Figures relate to launchings in the calendar year, with gross tonnage (merchant) and displacement tonnage (naval) added together.
Compiled from *Glasgow Herald Trade Review*
** Merchant figures only.

3. Output (horsepower)

Beardmore and main competitors

Year	Beardmore	Fairfield	Brown	Armstrong	Vickers	UK Total
1901	15,500	57,000	61,000			1,471,788
1902	27,900	45,750	24,500		9,340	1,309,601
1903		53,300	61,000		46,900	1,353,067
1904	2,500	36,485	28,900		32,250	1,338,972
1905	2,850	56,500	45,000		64,900	1,501,859
1906	4,000	29,380	108,900		79,000	1,846,003
1907	11,000	112,000	73,000		15,150	1,776,768
1908	10,000	20,460	41,750		58,850	1,145,545
1909	23,500	93,500	89,200		122,110	1,470,443
1910	26,500	100,200	77,700		90,000	1,623,032
1911	49,000	67,250	104,550		121,000	2,127,311
1912	60,000	55,200	178,500		136,750	2,272,266
1913	75,475	201,000	239,000		121,000	2,661,260
1914	105,100	220,280	197,500		136,900	1,366,834**
1915	93,130	202,610	319,000		136,100	540,594**
1916	122,600	468,410	349,400		74,140	
1917	141,200	195,880	282,400		150,320	
1918	167,760	291,160	313,600		82,000	4,322,200
1919	117,940	198,000	295,300	14,800	57,860	3,241,910
1920	25,986	38,350	31,700	20,000	35,350	1,700,106
1921	46,000	25,750	28,000	25,400	46,350	1,318,788
1922	30,740	20,700	19,050	46,150	12,000	812,466
1923	8,720		12,200	38,850	1,650	538,751
1924	29,880	25,200	56,850	4,050	36,100	1,104,254
1925	35,730	23,400	28,206	10,800	80,500	1,039,919
1926	82,920	92,000	21,550	10,800	93,700	1,028,018
1927	35,310	132,300	165,350	7,500	105,300	1,342,540
1928	90,800	104,850	67,850	18,400	31,700	1,907,821
1929	38,410	63,580	113,600	10,400	80,100	1,812,667
1930	44,000	19,600	147,000	46,700	111,700	1,880,223
1931	7,000	5,950		4,200	144,000	854,015
1932	36,400	72,000			144,000	682,656
1933			1,770		1,400	328,513
1934	146,100	46,200	85,170		102,900	1,487,682

Until 1905 at Govan, thereafter at Dalmuir.
Compiled from *Glasgow Herald Trade Review*
** Merchant figures only.

4. Capital Expenditure and Profit & Loss
by Departments. (£000)

Year	Shipyard	Engine	Artillery (1915/18)	Fuse (1915/17)	Loco (1920/30)	Aviation	Total	Profit (Loss)
1905	190,487	69,349						(3,337)
1906	89,693	23,379						(15,319)
1907	36,576	21,699						(122,692)
1908	4,643	,261						(64,195)
1909							6,359	(47,993)
1910							19,700	(6,868
1911	10,409	3,576					13,985	1,083
1912	2,772						23,934	(170,928)
1913							28,674	(163,347)
1914	13,075	18,181					31,256	(22,768)
1915	45,184	6,914	73,876	4,444			180,311	101,622
1916	13,831	8,845	129,657	4,674				118,840
1917	32,685	56,119	18,719	6,672				371,790
1918	60,917	80,826	5,702					470,684
1919	54,195	24,301			87,171			506,239
1920	46,698	4,457			91,573		329,183	(352,822)
1921	122,610						192,201	397,059
1922	1,133	,120			,329		1,612	275,009
1923	,409				,750		,559	(75,547)
1924	,753	,290				1,898	2,681	(369,787)
1925	,483	,717				,500	1,206	(143,866)
1926	,296				1,122 (H)	1,418		(243,878)
1927	,940	,311					1,251	(39,426)
1928	2,801	,755			,259		3,816	20,695
1929	6,341	21,101			,404		27,847	28,954

H = expenditure on plant to build steel houses

Dalmuir Empoyment Figures (where known)

1921	4183
1922	4182
1923	1896
1924	1501
1925	2457
1926	712
1927	1553
1928	4081
1929	2555
1930	1419

Source; Shipbuilding Employers Federation papers referring to 'new work' at Dalmuir – courtesy of Dr I Buxton.

5. Contracts List

All Departments (except Locomotive and Aviation after 1918). All contracts were given a number in chronological sequence irrespective of type of work. The yard numbers below served as ship numbers as well as gun or aircraft order numbers.

Yard No	Name/Description	Contract Price + extras	Cost	Profit (Loss)
484	Agamemnon	390,963	415,440	
485	Zaza	23,378	23,378	
486	Boilers for Almirante Grau (building at Vickers)			
487	-			
488	Quillota	160,804	170,455	(9,651)
489	Quilpué	"		
490	Huanchaco	135,259	143,770	(8,510)
491	Junin	"		
492	Orcoma	239,726	246,897	(7,171)
493	-			
494	Boilers for SS Constanza			(13,583)
495	Gloucester	301,537	271,394	30,142
496	Pharos	30,200	30,200	
497	Shieldhall	24,532	24,615	(,83)
498	Falmouth	282,199	273,588	8,611
499	Boilers	3,050	2,383	,666
500	Conqueror	876,535	832,386	44,148
501	Goshawk	85,933	81,015	4,917
502	2 Boilers for Rumanian State Railways	2,491	2,339	,152
503	Dublin	295,253	315,330	(20,077)
504	4 Boilers for Rumanian State Railways	5,900	4,809	1,091
505	Warilda	159,335	217,197	(57,862)
506	Wandilla	159,335	217,197	(57,862)
507	Willochra	159,335	217,197	(57,862)
508	Turbines for HMS Fearless (building at Pembroke)	109,487	117,560	(8,073)
509	Alsatian	467,254	596,232	(128,978)
510	Benbow	904,705	959,262	(54,556)
511	Llewellyn	99,541	104,517	(4,975)
512	Lennox	99,541	104,517	(4,975)
513	Galatea	332,445	313,217	19,227
514	Inconstant	332,445	313,217	19,227
515	Royalist	332,445	313,217	19,227
516	Ramillies	1,750,745	1,580,208	170,536
517	Experimental Ljungström turbines (Wulsty Castle)	2,500	2,752	(,252)
518	Nearchus	35,045	38,049	(3,003)
519	Argus	1,162,627	1,018,595	144,032
520	E25	98,953	67,488	31,465
521	E26	98,953	67,488	31,465
522	Clive	195,082	194,592	,490
523	Lawrence	162,865	162,347	,517
524	24 BE2c aircraft + 12 fuselages	37,471	29,137	8,333
525	270 18pdr Field guns excepting guns and breaches	603,299	541,536	61,762
526	Lassoo	149,801	128,373	21,427
527	Lochinvar	149,801	128,373	21,427
528	E53	111,120	94,873	16,247
529	E54	111,120	94,873	16,247
530	500 Leon mines (200 Admiralty 300 Russian Govt)	68,060	65,783	2,276
531	2 sets 8 cylinder diesels for E class submarines	14,209	9,603	4,605
532	12 Wight seaplanes	31,074	25,450	5,623
533	20 X Lighters (diesel driven barges)	166,400	100,874	65,525
534	6 x 4inch triple naval mountings for battlecruisers	37,000	30,160	6,839
535	-			
536	100 x 2 pdr gun mountings for Vickers	32,603	27,880	4,722
537	Pelican	158,444	136,495	21,949

Yard No	Name/Description	Contract Price + extras	Cost	Profit/Loss
538	Pellew	158,444	136,495	21,949
539	30 Sopwith Pup aircraft and 24 Seaplanes	50,842	32,230	18,612
540	3,000 fuses (written-off as valueless)			
541	86 aircraft	37,490	30,158	7,331
542	6inch Howitzers (quantity unknown)	122,279	116,555	5,724
543	90 x 18 pdr field gun carriages + limbers	37,619	12,353	25,265
544	8inch howitzers (quantity unknown)			
545	Airship No 24	161,683	145,131	16,552
546	P50	48,045	45,018	3,027
547	P51	48,045	45,018	3,027
548	2 boilers – P class paddle steamers (building at Cairds)	14,573	10,335	4,237
549	Satyr	170,722	150,103	20,619
550	Sharpshooter	170,722	150,103	20,619
551	Raleigh	1,385,225	1,270,286	114,938
552	70 Nieuport 12 aircraft	59,372	51,015	8,356
553	Airship No 27	131,321	115,107	16,241
554	Airship No 28 (cancelled)		10,000	
555	K16	354,177	272,221	81,955
556	Tancred	172,316	166,473	5,842
557	Tyrrhenia	1,359,907	1,220,908	138,998
558	Fuses	461,680	375,831	85,848
559	Turbines for HMS Tormentor (building at Stephen)	42,000	42,475	(,475)
560	Ulster	174,362	153,105	21,257
561	L6			
562	50 Sopwith Pup aircraft	35,612	29,105	6,507
563	Vancouver	208,435	188,788	19,646
564	Vanessa	208,435	188,788	19,646
565	HP4	63,161	60,679	2,481
566	HP5	63,161	60,679	2,481
567	HP6	63,161	60,679	2,481
568	HP7	63,161	60,679	2,481
569	Bearers for submarine engine	17,888	14,071	3,816
570	Vanity	207,295	183,123	24,170
571	Equipment for 18 pdr field guns	147,868	138,004	9,863
572	Leon mines (1922)	15,267	16,250	(,983)
573	110 x 6 inch howitzer gun carriages	319,883	282,121	37,762
574	12 Y Lighters (dumb barges 1917)	76,800	28,244	48,555
575	Airship R34	242,100	215,950	26,149
576	30 Sopwith Pup aircraft	21,000	20,321	,678
577	50 Mk IV tanks	197,500	190,109	7,390
578	Airship R36	269,358	240,163	29,915
579	100 WBIII aircraft	72,000	66,366	5,633
580	L69 (completed at Devonport)	115,722	106,748	9,243
581	L70 (cancelled)	72,972	62,683	10,288
582	Boilers for HMS Greyhound	5,617	6,679	(1,062)
583	4 x 12 cylinder diesel engines for L class submarines	19,800	12,603	7,196
584	Cameronia	1,389,254	1,275,115	114,139
585	Boilers for HMS Reindeer and Mariner	8,933	12,915	(3,982)
586	18 pdr carriages and limbers	248,958	107,434	141,523
587	6 Inch howitzer carriages and limbers	256,742	180,946	75,795
588	Engines for Mossend Works	-		
589	Tactician	200,517	179,921	20,596
590	Tara	200,517	179,921	20,596
645	Itaquicé	208,118		

Yard No	Name/Description	Contract Price + extras	Cost	Profit/Loss
591	Tasmania	200,517	179,921	20,596
592	Tattoo	200,517	179,921	20,596
593	H47			
594	H48			
595	H49			
596	H50			
597	Four boilers for Edward Finch	14,000	11,601	2,398
598	150 Sopwith Camel aircraft	113,925	88,275	25,649
599	Vansittart	232,915	214,798	18,116
600	Vimy	172,549	153,998	18,550
601	60 Handley Page V/1500 bombers (40 cancelled)	274,022	245,780	28,241
602	Daring (cancelled)	80,466	76,550	3,915
603	Desperate (cancelled)			
604	Vashon (cancelled)	37,745	37,236	,508
605	Vengeful	37,745	37,236	,508
606	L59		15,000	
607	18 pdr Mk III gun carriages	442,250	359,071	83,178
608	3 sets of standard boilers	27,497	29,898	(2,400)
609	30 Sopwith Camel aircraft	26,732	30,926	(4,193)
610	fuses	3,326	2,247	1,079
611	Conte Rosso	1,526,378	1,473,952	52,426
612	Conte Verde	-		
613	Setter	118,293	135,225	(16,932)
614	Airship R40 (cancelled)	3,981	4,201	(,219)
615	Hannah E Reynolds (speculative) later sold for £7,000 to Leith & Aberdeen owners,			
616	Largs Bay	1,147,258	1,046,554	100,703
617	Esperance Bay	1,085,504	986,648	98,855
618	Pinzon	139,689		
619	Pizarro	138,759		
620	-			
621	British Trader	272,650	251,197	21,452
622	British Merchant	352,916	328,677	24,239
623	British Enterprise	247,315	227,361	19,953
624	British Industry	225,420	211,083	14,337
625	British Commerce	217,701	203,966	13,735
626	Engines for Forth Shipbuilding Co			
627	G3 battlecruiser (cancelled) Accounts record £1,744 9s,7d against wages and material			
628	Henry Ward			
629	Beardmore diesel for mv Silurian (building at Blythswood)	50,000		
630	Arcoona	76,636		
631	Allara	73,859		
632	Generator sets for HMS Nelson (building at Armstrongs)	20,014		
633	Carlotta	62,747		
634	Krisjanis Valdemars	107,400		
635	Hebble	43,500		
636	Rye	43,500		
637	Ulooloo			
638	Conchita			
639	Turbines for HMS Cornwall (building at Devonport)	461,932		
640	Conte Biancamano			
641	Casandra			
642	Chepita			
643	John Perring	32,636		
644	Itapé			

Yard No	Name/Description	Contract Price + extras	Cost	Profit/Loss
645	Itaquicé	208,118		
646	Itanagé	207,957		
647	Shropshire	1,099,644		
648	Duchess of Atholl			
649	Olympus	287,200		
650	Orpheus	295,205		
651	Manunda			
652	Salford City			
653	Havaco			
654	Hydraulic clutches for submarines	47,510		
655	Northgate Scot			
656	Royalist (cancelled) Accounts record £17,269 spent on wages and materials			
657	Engines for Asperity (building at George Brown & Co, Greenock)			
658	Romany Rye	80,246		
659	Engines for H Williamson & Co	8,055		
660	Virginia	21,915		
661	Dalhanna	91,460		
662	Daldorch	91,460		
663	Pole Star			
664	Machinery for HMS Duncan (building at Portsmouth Dockyard)			
665	Diesel engines for Wulsty Castle			
666	Machinery for HMS Amphion (building at Portsmouth Dockyard)			
667	Machinery for HMS Apollo (building at Devonport Dockyard)			
668	Machinery for HMS Speedwell (building at Hamiltons)			

In the mid 1920s accountancy practice altered making the identification of individual contracts difficult to determine.

6. Aircraft 1915 – 1919

Built under sub-contract at Dalmuir, Inchinnan and Dumfries (Arrol Johnston)

Type	Role	Quantity	Span x length/weight all up engines/armament
RAF BE2c	Two-seat reconnaissance	60	37' x 27' 3" 2,142lb 1 x 70hp Renault or 90hp RAF, 72mph 224lb of bombs 1 MG
Sopwith Pup	Single-seat fighter	80	26'6" x 19' 3.75" 1,225lb 80hp Clerget or 80hp Le Rhône 9c, 111mph 1 Lewis MG and or 8 Le Prieur rockets
Sopwith 2F.1 Camel	Single-seat ship's fighter	175	28' x 18'9" 1,453lb 150hp BR1 or 130hp Clerget, 115mph 2 MG
Wight 840	Seaplane	32	61' x 41' 4,453 lb 225hp Sunbeam, 81mph 1 x 14" torpedo
Nieuport 12	Two-seat Fighter/reconnaissance	50	29' 7.5" x 23' 6" 2,028lb 110hp Clerget 9Z, 98mph, 2 MG
Handley Page V/1500	4 engined bomber	20	126' x 62' 24,700lb 4 x 375hp Rolls-Royce Eagle 30 x 250lb bombs, 6 MG, 4 crew

1915 – 1919

Designed by Beardmore at Dalmuir

Type	Role	Quantity	Span x Length/weight all up engines/armament
WB I	Two-seat bomber biplane	1	61'6" x 32' 10" 5,600lb 1 x 240hp Sunbeam or 230hp Beardmore Adriatic, 91mph 1 x .303 Lewis gun. 6 x 100lb bombs
WB IA	Two-seat bomber biplane	not built	70' x 38'1" 8,900lb 1 x 515hp Beardmore Pacific V12, 110mph 6 x 250lb bombs, 3 x 100lb bombs 2 x .303 Lewis guns
WB II	Two-seat fighter reconnaissance biplane	1	34' 10" x 27' 3" 2,650 lb 1 x 200hp Hispano Suiza or 230hp Beardmore Adriatic, 120mph 2 x Vickers MG, 1 x .303 Lewis gun
WBIIA	Two-seat fighter biplane	not built	35' x 27' 7" 2,700lb 1 x 230hp Beardmore Adriatic, 125mph 2 x Vickers MG, 1 x .303 Lewis gun
WBIIB	Two-seat passenger biplane	2 G-EARX and G-EARY	34'10" x 27'7" 2,516lb 160hp Beardmore, 107 mph
WBIII SBIIIF (first 2) SBIIID (other 98)	Single seat, shipboard fighter with folding wings and undercarriage " " jettisonable u/carriage	100	25' x 20' 2.5" 1,290lb 1 x 80hp Le Rhône or Clerget rotary, 103 mph. 1 x .303 Lewis gun

Type	Role	Quantity	Span x length/weight all up engines/armament
WBIV	Single-seat, torpedo biplane with folding wings and flotation compartment in forward fuselage for emergency ditchings	1	35' x 26'6" 2,600lb 1 x 200hp Hispana Suiza, 110mph 1 x .303 Lewis gun 1 x Vickers MG
WBV	Single-seat, shipboard fighter with folding wings	2	35' 10" x 26' 7" 2,500lb 1 x 200hp Hispana Suiza, 112mph 1 x .303 Lewis, 1 x Vickers MG
WBVI	Single-seat, torpedo biplane with folding wings	not built	53'6.5" x 34' 5,637lb 1 x 360hp Rolls-Royce Eagle, 102mph 1 x 1800lb torpedo
WBV1a	Passenger biplane with folding wings	not built	62' x 42' 6" 7,330lb 1 x 500hp Beardmore, 120mph 6 passengers, 2 crew
WBV1b	Passenger biplane with folding wings	not built	36' x 27' 3' 2,680lb 1 x 160hp Beardmore, 108mph 2 passengers and pilot
WBV1c	Single-seat biplane	not built	21' x 15' 7" 770lb 1 x 45hp ABC Gnat, 98mph
WBV1d	Passenger biplane with folding wings	not built	62' x 45' 4" 6,832lb 2 x 200hp Beardmore, 102mph 6 passengers, 2 crew
WBVII	existence not confirmed		
WBVIII	Passenger cargo triplane	not built	120' x 62' 27,320lb 3 x 500hp Beardmore Atlantics V12, 92mph, 24 passengers, 5 crew. 2,800lb cargo
WBIX	Passenger seaplane (G-EAQI)	1 (not completed)	107' x 61' 14,000lb 4x200hp Beardmore, 93mph 10 passengers and pilot
WBX	Two-seat all-metal biplane (G-EAQJ)	1	46' x 26' 2,849lb 1 x 185hp Beardmore, 91mph
WBXXIV	Two-seat monoplane 'Wee Bee" G-EBJJ	1	38'10" x 22'2" 840lb 1 x 1,096cc Bristol Cherub, 87mph
WBXXVI	Two-seat fighter biplane	1	37' x 27'10.5" 3,980lb 1 x Rolls-Royce Eagle IX 145 mph 3 Beardmore Farquhar machine guns
WB–	All-metal single-seat monoplane fighter	not built	1 x Bristol Jupiter MkV
WB–	All-metal two-seat monoplane reconnaissance seaplane	not built	1 x Rolls-Royce Eagle IX

Type	Role	Quantity	Span x length/weight all up engines/armament
BeRo1 Inflexible	Experimental all-metal monoplane	1 (J7557)	156'7" x 82'9" 31,400lb 3 x 650hp Rolls-Royce Condor III V12 104mph. 2 crew
BeRo2 Inverness	Experimental all-metal monoplane flying boat	1 (N184)	96'9" x 54' 13,160lb 2 x 450hp Napier Lion V12, 110mph 2 crew

War built aircraft in batches as ordered

Aircraft	Quantity	Numbers	Year	Notes
RAF BE2c	24	1099 to 1122	1915	
Wight 840 seaplanes	12	1400 to 1411	1915	
RAF BE2c	12	8326 to 8337	1915	
RAF BE2c	13	8488 to 8500	1915	
RAF BE2c	11	8714 to 8724	1915	
Wight 840 seaplanes	20	9021 to 9040	1915	9029 to 9040 delivered as spare parts
Nieuport 12	50	9201 to 9250	1915	
Sopwith Pup	50	9901 to 9950	1916/17	
WBIV	3	N38 to N40	1917	N39 and N40 not completed
WBV	3	N41 to N43	1917	N43 cancelled or not completed
WBI	1	N525	1916	
WBII	1	-	1915/16	Not allocated a number
WBIII	30	N6100 to N6129	1917	
Sopwith Pup	30	N6430 to N6459	1917	
WBIII	70	N6680 to N6749	1917	42 cancelled but later reinstated, however most of these went into storage
Sopwith 2F.1 Camel	50	N6750 to N6799	1917	
Sopwith 2F.1 Camel	50	N6800 to N6849	1917	
Sopwith 2F.1 Camel	40	N7100 to N7139	1918	
Sopwith 2F.1 Camel	10	N7140 to N7149	1918	Built by Arrol Johnston, Dumfries
Sopwith 2F.1 Camel	50	N7350 to N7399	1918	Built by Arrol Johnston. N7375 to N7399 cancelled
Sopwith 2F.1 Camel	30	N7650 to N7679	1918	All cancelled November 1918
Handley Page V/1500	20	E8287 to E8306	1918	Assembled at Inchinnan or delivered as spare parts
Handley Page V/1500	30	E8201 to E8230	1918	All cancelled

On the reopening of the Aviation Department in 1924, the contracts were numbered as follows;

Works No	Aircraft	Contract Price
AV1	Inflexible	40,000
AV2	'Wee Bee'	—
AV3	Latvian Fighter	3,500 (7,357 spent until December 1925)
AV4	—	—
AV5	Inverness	32,100 (Delivery flight to Felixstowe cost £31.13s)

7. Airships

No	Class	Role	Dimensions/volume lift/armament	Laid down Completed	Fate
24	23	Recconnaisance	535' x 53' diameter 899,650ft³, lift 27.3t. 4 x 100lb bombs, 1 x 2pdr 4 x Lewis guns 4 x 250hp Wolseley 55mph	21/07/16 -	
27	23X	"	539'3" x 53' diameter 941,000ft³, lift 28.5t 20 x 112lb bombs, 1x 2pdr 4 x Lewis guns 4 x 250hp Rolls-Royce 55mph	16/03/17 08/04/ /06/18 (first flight)	Burnt-out in shed at Howden 16/08/18 Total flight time logged 90hrs
28	23X	"	"		Cancelled August 1917
R34	R33	"	643' x 78' 9" diameter 1,950,000ft³. lift 59.2t Disposable lift 24 t 5 x 250hp Sunbeam Maori 65 mph	09/12/17 20/12/18 14/03/19 (first flight)	Scrapped following damage received during gale at Howden, 27 January 1921 Total flight time logged 500hrs
R36	R35	passenger	672'2" x 78'9" diameter 2,196,000ft³ lift 64.5t 2 x 260hp Maybach, 3 x 335hp Sunbeam Cossack 65 mph 50 passengers, 28 crew	- 01/04/21 21/06/21.	Damaged after overshooting mooring mast at Pulham on Kept in shed until 1925 when scrapped Total flight time logged 80hrs
R40	R38	"	695' x 85'4" diameter 2,750,000ft³ lift 83t Disposable lift 50t 6 x 335mph Sunbeam Cossack 70mph		Cancelled 20/08/19

8. Locomotives

Contr. No	Qty	Works No	Built for	Year	Wheels	Gauge	Railway Numbers
L1	35	100-134	East India Railway Co	1920	2-8-0	5'6"	1520-1554
L2	20	135-154	Great Eastern Railway Co	1920/21	4-6-0	Std	1541-1560
L3	19	155-173	Nigerian Railways	1920	4-8-0	3'6"	282-300
L4	90	174-263	London & North Western Rly Co	1921	4-6-0	Std	see below
L5	5	264-268	Burma Railway Co Ltd	1923	0-6-6-0	Metre	16-20
L6	25	269-293	Bombay Baroda & Central India Rly	1923	4-6-0	5'6"	540-564
L7	2	294-295	Madras & Southern Mahratta Rly	1923	4-6-0	5'6"	784,785
L8	3	296-298	East Bengal State Railway	1923	4-6-0	5'6"	31-33
L9	5	299-303	North Western Railway of India	1923	4-6-0	5'6"	2875-2879
L10	1	304	London Midland & Scottish Railway	1924	4-6-0	Std	5845
L11	20	305-324	London & North Eastern Railway	1927	0-6-2T	Std	2642-2661
L16/17	90	325-414	London Midland & Scottish Railway	1927	0-6-0T	Std	16600-16624, 16685-16749
L18	2	415-416	Bombay Baroda & Central India Rly	1928	Bo-Bo	5'6"	901,902 (Battery Electrics)
L23	43	417-460	East Indian Railway	1928	2-8-2	5'6"	1981-2003,2016-2036
L29	25	461-486	North Western Railway of India	1929/30	4-6-2	5'6"	1842-1867
"	4	487-490	Bombay Baroda & Central India Rly	1930	4-6-2	5'6"	613-616
"	2	491-492	East Indian Railway	1930	4-6-2	5'6"	1948,1949
L30	2	492-493	North Western Railway of India	1930	Bo-Bo	5'6"	330,331 (Diesels)

LNWR numbers in sequence as built by Beardmore: 120, 123, 125, 129, 135, 140, 142, 145, 148, 224, 227,232, 237, 239-244, 246-249, 251, 252, 258-259, 261, 266, 394, 267-270, 272-274, 277, 281, 292, 293, 296, 313, 324, 325, 331, 355, 357, 359, 435, 436, 438, 440, 442, 443, 452, 483, 489, 490, 284, 491, 557, 493, 549, 492, 514, 17, 551, 554, 558, 153, 198, 354, 778, 1099, 1179, 1316, 1339, 1349, 53, 197, 433, 614, 1083, 1320, 1323, 1344, 1742, 2043.

Caprotti Valve Gear Contracts were numbered:
L12 to L15
L25 to L28
L31 to L32

Locomotives known to have been repaired at Dalmuir:
Ministry of Supply	0-6-0T quantity unknown
Glasgow & South Western Railway	4-4-0 several, including No 355
Glasgow & South Western Railway	0-6-0 No 367
London & North Western Railway	0-8-0 No 1881
North British Railway	0-6-0T No 821
North British Railway	0-6-2T No 251
Caledonian Railway	0-6-0T No 787
Highland Railway	4-6-0 No 141 (rebuilt)
Highland Railway	4-4-0 No 94 and 95
Highland Railway	0-6-0 No 19

9. Steel Houses

Works No	Year	Quantity	Customer	Contract Price
H1-9	1926	50		
H10-21	1926	50	Atholl Steel Houses Ltd	£23,452
H22	1927		(houses for erection at Dalmuir)	

Company records are very incomplete with respect to Atholl Steel Houses. Many were ordered by many councils throughout Scotland. At least 100 were built in Clydebank the first being let between June and September 1927

10. Buildings at Dalmuir Shipyard 1901-1924

Approximate building sequence. Unless otherwise stated, dates are those in which building approval was granted. Based on records held by Clydebank District Council.

Year	Month	Description
1901	October	New road to Clyde Trust Workshops (Clutha Street)
	November	Temporary site offices for James Goldie & Co
	Nov/Dec	Work on fitting-out basin commences
1902	January	Levelling at site, piling at riverside
	June	150 ton Hammerhead crane ordered
	March	Engine and boiler works
	April	Gas plant, producers and Power Station
	September	Stonework at fitting-out basin complete, excavation about to start
	December	Platers Shed
1904	January	Timber Shed
	February	Joiners Shop, Paint Shop, Riggers Loft, Boat Shed
	April	Smithy, Angle Iron Smiths Admiralty Store, General Store and Mould Loft. Overhead gas pipes
	May	Fitting-out basin flooded. 150 ton crane almost completed
	June	Mechanics and Brass Finishers Shop. Overhead gas pipes to engine works
	June	Cooling tower at gas plant. Electrical workshop and offices
	July	Pattern Shop, Hammerhead crane completed
	August	General Offices at Park Road
	September	Plumbers shop, Sheet Iron Shop
	October	Shipbuilding gantry and other berths
	October	Store and laboratory
	December	3 tenements and 1 road (Agamemnon Street) 3 new roads and 34 tenements
	November	Sawmill
1905	June	Pattern store and time office
	October	Power station extension
1906	June	4 tenements at Dumbarton Road
1907	January	18 tenements at Dumbarton Road
1909	January	Shed at boiler shop
1910	July	Road to former Clyde Trust Workshops closed (Clutha Street)
1911	May	Pumping house. Gas cooling tower
1912		New berths formed, eight 5 ton derrick cranes purchased, 30 ton travelling dock crane purchased
	December	Copper Shop
1913	February	Covered berths at West Yard
1914	November	Beam Shed, West Yard platers shed (first two of four berths). Machine shop (for manufacture of guns)
1915	January	Covered berths at West Yard (two additional berths). Field Carriage Shop
	February	Blade Shop
	March	Seaplane sheds
	May	The Benbow Hotel
	April	Machine shop extension (for manufacture of guns)
	August	Gun Mounting Shop
	September	Fuse works
	October	Gun Sight Shop
	November	Galleries in Seaplane shed
1915/20		71 tenements and 6 new roads Castle Square, Kitchener Street, Jellicoe Street, Beatty Street, French Street
1916	January	Hangars at Robertson Park
	October	Dock workshop

Year	Month	Description
1917	-	Tank Shop, Riggers Store, Pipe Shop, Brass Foundry, Torpedo Shop, Howitzer Shop, Inspection Shop
	January	Workshop at West Yard
	February	Extension at seaplane shed.
1918	-	Compressor house, managers time office
	February	Extensions to main platers shed and mechanics shop
	March	Aeroplane packing shed. Dope room
	March	Extension at seaplane shed
	August	Locomotive steaming shed
1919	September	Gun shops altered to locomotive works
1920		New number 6 berth. Six 5 ton derricks, five 3 ton derricks. Engine works canteen, managers office and drawing office. East Yard managers office, time offices and power station. Four 'Toplis' cranes
	May	East Yard platers shed and template shed. Gantries over rough material yard
	June	Packing Shop, rough material store
	October	Electric welding house
	July	New general store
1924	October	'Atholl House' steel bungalow

11. The Re-use and Reduction of Dalmuir Shipyard 1907-1992
(approximate dates only)

Year	Description
1907-	Part demolition of Clyde Trust Workshops by Beardmore to make way for new graving dock
1920	Removal of earthworks and buildings associated with Fuse Works by Beardmore to make way for new East Yard
1931-32	Sale of plant and equipment at shipyard including all derricks and fixed Toplis cranes
1933	Demolition of shipbuilding gantry
1934	East Yard briefly used by Arnott Young for shipbreaking
	East wall of fitting-out basin, Joiners shop, Plumbers shop, Timber shed, 30 ton wharf crane and other smaller buildings in vicinity used by Arnott Young for ship-breaking
1938 -	East Yard purchased by GPO. Berths excavated and formed into tidal basin. East yard platers shed converted to offices and stores.
	Turners Asbestos Cement Co acquire main platers shed. Buildings converted and extended for the manufacture of asbestos sheet material. Aviation sheds used for asbestos fibre storage
1939-	Engine Works and Locomotive Works acquired by War Department and re-equipped for the manufacture of armour plate and ordnance. All buildings between Engine works and fitting-out basin demolished. Wharfs and slips at submarine sheds and former Clyde Trust piers filled-in. River Clyde returned to original line (i.e. straight). Large engineering shops erected on ground reclaimed and cleared to become part of Royal Ordnance Factory. West wall of fitting-out basin and 150 ton crane retained as part of ROF
1941	Former General Office and Joiners Shop destroyed during Clydebank Blitz. New buildings later erected in their place. The Benbow Hotel and several former Beardmore tenements at west of Dalmuir destroyed in Blitz
1939-45	West wall of fitting-out basin used by John Brown and several other shipbuilders to complete ships
1959	Babcock and Wilcox lease all ROF buildings following closure of works and commence manufacturing.
1962	Turners Asbestos Cement Co extend asbestos manufacturing capacity at Dalmuir adding new buildings
1970	Babcock discontinue manufacturing. Ministry of Defence sell works to Ministry of Technology.
1971-	Entire ROF site demolished from 1971 onwards. Clydebank Industrial Estate created being developed by Scottish Industrial Estates. (150 ton crane pulled over and scrapped in 1972)
	Turners cease manufacture. Proposals to develop former asbestos works into caravan sales centre and associated leisure goods not realised
1975	Scottish Development Agency take over CIE and further develop site
	By 1980, the site between the fitting-out basin and eastern boundary is divided into four areas – Arnott Young, Monaville Estates (Turners), Riverside Industrial Estate (based on former Sawmill) and the GPO (based on former East Yard)
1981	Entire Beardmore site included in Clydebank Enterprise Zone.
1984	Arnott Young (now part of Tarmac Group) cease shipbreaking. This site acquired by SDA in 1987
1989	By 1989 all original shipyard buildings from fitting-out basin to the GPO demolished.
1989/90	Fitting-out basin filled in. The north bank of the Clyde at Dalmuir, with the exception of GPO basin, generally resembles pre 1860 state
1991	Work commences on construction of hospital on approximate site of main shipyard berths
1993	Only three buildings remain to mark the existence of Beardmore's Naval Construction Works

Left. The last remaining buildings of the Naval Construction Works in what is now Cable Depot Road. The east yard time and managers office (left) with the bricked-up windows of the power station beyond.
Right. The three bay roof of the east yard platers shed. Photographed in 1992.

12. The 1912 Beardmore Seaplane Carrier Proposal
(Preliminary Submission 23 October 1912 as transcribed from original document)

OUTLINE SPECIFICATION FOR A PROPOSED PARENT SHIP FOR NAVAL AEROPLANES

Principal Dimensions

Length between perpendiculars	450 feet
Breadth extreme	110 feet
Breadth at waterline	90 feet
Depth, moulded to upper deck	31 feet
Draft, mean, normal	20 feet
Displacement, normal, in tons, about	11,500
Speed on trial (knots)	21
SHP on trial (about)	22,000

General Description

The vessel is to be constructed generally in accordance with the accompanying sketch plan* and to more fully detailed plans and specifications as may be hereafter mutually agreed upon.

To have ram stem, elliptical stern, shelter, upper, protective and platform decks.

The protective deck extends for the full length of the vessel for the protection of the machinery, boilers, shell rooms, magazines, auxiliary machinery and other vital parts of the ship.

Thick protective plating of high tensile steel is to be fitted on the sides of the vessel in addition to the protective decks, as described hereafter.

The hull both above and below the protective deck to be efficiently subdivided by means of transverse and longitudinal watertight bulkheads, watertight flats, etc.

A cellular double bottom to extend under engines and boilers and well forward and aft of same beneath boilers and magazines and shell rooms. The compartments of double bottom in way of machinery spaces where practicable to be utilised for stowage of reserve feed water and liquid fuel.

Below the protective deck coal bunkers are to be arranged alongside boiler rooms. Above the protective deck the coal bunkers are to be arranged for the extent indicated on drawings.

The armament, as hereafter specified, to be placed generally as shown on plans. The arrangement permits of great concentration of fire and large arcs of training.

Suitable magazine and other stowage to be provided for shot, shell, cordite, torpedoes, etc., well protected and with all necessary arrangements for flooding, ventilating etc.

Torpedo net defence is to be arranged for the extent indicated on the drawings.

Two steel lower masts with wood topmasts, spars etc., to be fitted having wireless telegraphy apparatus complete. Derricks etc., to be fitted to masts for working boats.

Two electrically driven cranes to be provided and fitted aft for lifting aeroplanes on board.

Steam capstan gear to be fitted forward and electric gear aft. A powerful installation of electric engines and dynamos and other auxiliary machinery, to be provided as required for lighting and ventilating the ship, cooling magazines, working guns, ammunition hoists, etc.

Two sets of turbine engines, placed in two separate engine rooms as shown on plans, driving two shafts, supplied with steam from an installation of 16 watertube boilers arranged in three separate boiler rooms to be provided.

The vessel to be constructed generally of mild steel of best quality, and all material used throughout the construction of the vessel and her machinery, etc,. to be of the very best description, equal in every respect to those supplied for similar vessels of the ~British Navy and to stand the same tests.

Armament

The armament to consist of the following:-

12 – 6 inch 50 calibre B.L. guns with open backed shields mounted six forward and six aft on superstructures as per plan, with stowage for 150 rounds of ammunition per gun.

4- 47mm Q.F. Aeroplane Guns with stowage for 300 rounds per gun.

4 – Maxim R.C. with stowage for 5,000 rounds per gun.

4 – 21 inch Submerged Torpedo Tubes, two on each broadside with stowage for three torpedoes for each tube.

All the usual small arms and ammunition. For the main armament an end on fire of 4 guns forward and 4 guns aft is provided and a broadside fire of 6 guns on each side.

The supply of ammunition to the guns is to be carefully considered, and a suitable number of hoists to be provided leading direct to the upper deck as far as practicable in the immediate vicinity of the guns.

The 47mm Q.F. Guns are to be mounted on pedestal mountings on the superstructure deck, in suitable positions, and some of the larger boats will be arranged to mount these guns.

The Maxim machine guns will be mounted on the superstructure and on some of the larger boats.

The 21 inch Submerged Torpedo Tubes are disposed one on each broadside forward and aft. They are suitable for discharging the latest pattern 21 inch torpedo fitted with heater arrangement

---

*no copy of the sketch plan was found

for increasing speed and range.

Conning Towers

Two conning towers are to be constructed of armour 3 inches thick and placed on superstructure under ends of bridge. The roof to be 1 inch thick and the floor 1 inch thick.

Protective Deck

The protective deck is to be formed of one thickness of steel 1 inch thick on flat and 2 inches thick on slopes. The plating is to be of high tensile steel.

Protective Plating of Side

The side plating amidships for length of hangars and workshop spaces to be formed of two thicknesses of high tensile steel of a combined total thickness of 3 inches extending from edge of shelter deck at side to upper deck.

Speed

The vessel to maintain a speed of 21 knots on extended trial of 8 hours duration under conditions similar to those laid down by the British Admiralty.

Propelling Machinery

The main propelling machinery would consist of two sets of Parsons Compound Steam Turbines of the impulse reaction type arranged in two engine rooms, and each driving one propeller. Condensing plant to be the 'Weir' 'Uniflux' type with air and circulating pumps are fitted capable of producing and maintaining a vacuum in the condensers of 95% Barometric Height with sea water at a temperature of 13*C.

Steam is produced in 16 watertube boilers of the Yarrow Small Tube Type in three compartments. During the eight hours full speed high power trial the boilers are to produce the necessary steam when working under the closed stokehold system of forced draught and burning coal and oil fuel.

The Auxiliary Machinery for the working of engines and boilers would consist of the necessary filters, heaters, feed pumps, fire and bilge and ash ejector pumps, oil fuel pumps, boiler tube sweeping compressor, ash ejector and distilling machinery.

Searchlights

Searchlights, 4 in number, of 36 inched diameter, hand controlled, are to be provided and arranged, to be worked in conjunction with the armament as necessary.

Boats

The following motor and sailing boats to be provided complete, and suitably stowed. Some of the larger boats to be arranged to mount the lighter pattern guns

4 – Motor Boats	length	45 feet
2 – Sailing Cutters	length	30 feet
2 – Sailing Gigs	length	24 feet
2 – Sailing Whalers	length	27 feet
2 – Sailing Dinghies	length	18 feet

Hangars etc, for Aeroplanes

Hangars are to be constructed on each side of the ship of the size indicated on the plans, to stow 6 naval aeroplanes complete, ready for use. In addition to these hangars a store room is provided for spare parts of planes and spare planes, and another store room for spare motors with workshop for repairs etc. The front of the hangars, workshop etc., will be protected by steel Venetian shutters, stiffened on the inside by portable 'T' bars, and having canvas screens securely fastened on the outside to render them waterproof at sea. A portable coaming will be fitted along the front of the hangars, etc., at the lower edge of the shutters to rest against.

For the length of the deck indicated on the drawings rails will be fitted to take the loose carriage of aeroplanes. Turntables will be fitted opposite the centre of each hangar so that planes may be turned when being brought out of hangar for use or returning to hangar for stowage. At the forward and after ends hydraulic buffers or other suitable arrangement will be fitted to stop the carriages. The carriages will be arranged to take the base of the aeroplanes, one being provided for each hangar. They will have a special releasing device, such that when the plane is running along the deck it will not be able to leave the carriage until it passes a releasing lever which will come into operation when the tail of the aeroplane is absolutely clear of the superstructure. An automatic breaking arrangement could also be fitted to come into play after the carriage is run close up to the buffers at the forward end.

The motor boats are available for use in bringing the aeroplanes within the radius of the cranes at the after end which would then lift them from the water and place them on the loose carriage running on the rails on the upper deck. The boat hoisting derricks are also available for lifting the aeroplanes if necessary.

A large stowage is provided for stowage of petrol in cases or in bulk as may hereafter be decided upon. If required, a stowage could also be provided for stowage of bombs.

A good sheer has been given to the vessel forward and this will allow the loose carriages automatically to run back to the hangars and the camber on the deck also allows the carriages to run out easily towards the stowing position in the hangars.

The forecastle deck forward would be kept absolutely clear with portable rails And stanchions at sides only, the anchor and cable gear being fitted to work on the deck below.

[On 19 December 1912, a 110 page detailed specification was submitted to the Admiralty for consideration. Titled 'Specification For Building the Hull and Completing a Parent Ship for Naval Aeroplanes and Torpedo Boat Destroyers', the vessel described in this document differed considerably from that above. The general description only from this document is printed below – author]

Principal Dimensions

Length between perpendiculars	430 feet
Breadth extreme	110 feet
Depth moulded to shelter deck	38 feet
Displacement at load water line	15,000 tons

General Description

The vessel is designed to act as a parent vessel for naval aeroplanes and torpedo boat destroyers and is to be constructed generally with this specification and accompanying plans with straight stem, elliptical stern, Bridge, Shelter, Upper, Main, Lower and Orlop Decks.

The hull to be efficiently subdivided by means of watertight bulkheads, flats etc., and a c cellular double bottom to extend under engines and boilers and well forward and aft under magazines, shell rooms etc., being omitted in way of oil fuel compartments. Under the engine and boiler rooms and forward and aft of the machinery spaces, compartments suitably subdivided are to be arranged for the stowage of liquid fuel. The wing compartments are to extend to the level of the main deck, and the centre compartments to the upper deck.

Bridge houses are to be built on each side of the ship on the shelter deck of the height and to the extent indicated on the drawings. They are to be subdivided and arranged as hangars for aeroplanes, workshops, storerooms, etc., as shown. Gangway doors to be fitted through ship's side at each workshop. 8 – 4 inch

50 calibre Q.F. guns with shields to be mounted on Bridge Deck, 4 on each broadside as shown on plans or as may be hereafter decided upon.

At the ends of the vessel below the waterline compartments are to be arranged for the stowage of spare aeroplanes, also spare torpedoes, torpedo heads and ammunition for torpedo boat destroyers. 4 electric ammunition hoists to be provided for working ammunition and ensuring ready supply to the guns mounted on Bridge Deck.

Two steel lower masts with wood top masts, spars etc., to be fitted and equipped with a specially powerful installation of wireless telegraphy apparatus. A steel derrick and two electric winches to be fitted at each mast for working boats, shipping and unshipping heavy weights, etc., 4 electric cranes are also to be provided, 2 at each end of the vessel for lifting aeroplanes on board and shipping or unshipping lighter loads.

Two fenders are provided on each side of the vessel to enable destroyers to lie alongside when fuelling or undergoing repairs. A portable gangway is also arranged abreast each gangway door of sufficient length to rest on the deck of a destroyer lying alongside.

Steam capstan gear to be fitted forward suitable for working the anchors and cables. The engine to be placed on main deck with cable holders, capstans etc., on upper deck so as to give the shelter deck a clear run for aeroplanes taking off.

Four steam capstans are provided, two forward and two aft at sides of shelter deck for mooring or warping ship or destroyers alongside and general purposes.

Steam and hand steering gear with telemotor control gear is arranged on upper deck aft so as to have shelter deck clear for working aeroplanes.

Hatches are provided where required for shipping aeroplanes, stores, ammunition, torpedoes etc. These hatches are to be flush at shelter deck and trunked where necessary.

Two large electric hoists are arranged connecting the repair store rooms on main deck with the workshops on shelter deck.

A large sick bay, a bakery, refrigerated provision chambers and other store rooms are arranged to meet the requirements of a flotilla of destroyers and enable them to keep the sea for extended periods, the oil fuel compartments being of sufficient capacity to replenish the tanks of the whole of the vessels forming a flotilla.

A powerful installation of electric engines and dynamos,

air-compressing and refrigeration machinery, etc., to be provided for lighting and ventilating ship, driving workshop machinery, working hoists, cooling magazines and cold chambers, etc.,

The propelling machinery is to consist of two sets of Parsons geared turbines driving two shafts and supplied with steam from an installation of four watertube boilers arranged to burn oil fuel. To be capable of developing sufficient power to drive the vessel at a speed of not less than 15 knots on trial (as specified hereafter)

Simple plan of the second seaplane carrier proposal from a sketch by TNS Dickson.

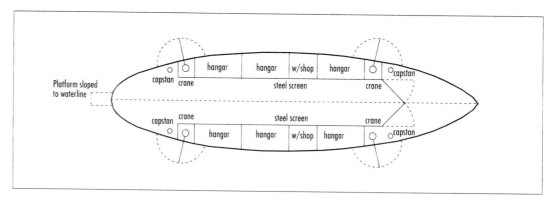

REFERENCES AND NOTES

NAVAL CONSTRUCTION WORKS

1   Early references to Beardmore's expansion into shipbuilding at Dalmuir mention a 'gun factory'
     as part of the scheme. *Clydebank Press* 24 August 1900 p5. The *Clydebank Press* of 3 April 1903
     p5 also reports that Beardmore was negotiating with a view to establishing a shipyard in Sydney,
     Nova Scotia.
2   Scott, JD. *Vickers: A History* p49.
3   *Engineer*, 2 January 1903 p6 – Dalmuir.
4   Napier & Miller at Old Kilpatrick in 1905, Yarrow at Scotstoun in 1906 and Blythswood at
     Scotstoun in 1919.
5   MacLeod, Donald. *Clyde District of Dunbartonshire*. Dunbarton, 1886.
6   Strathclyde Regional Council Archives, Clyde Navigation Trust Papers TCN 12 632 – contract
     to erect works by John Coghill 1865. The Clyde Navigation Trust acquired 8 acres of land at
     Dalmuir Shore from William Dunn of Duntocher. This site had been the location of a soda works
     established by Lord Dundas at the end of the 18th Century. As completed in 1867 the workshops
     included the following; patent slip; smiths shop, machine shop, iron store and sawmill all under
     one roof; shed for buoys, tumblers and boats; shed for large boilers and plate furnace; saw pit shed
     and carpenters shop all under one roof; shed for punts at repairing slip; engine and boiler house
     at slip; pole and oar shed; pitch and tar store; dining shed for men; offices, porters room, pattern
     store and joiners shop all in a two storey building at the works entrance gate. There was a basin
     of 1.25 acres and an additional slip for hauling up very small craft. Wrought iron work used in
     building the works was specified to be 'Govan best' The total cost of the works was £11,702 17s.
     By 1880 the works employed 226 people. In 1894 a new engine and boiler shop was added.
7   Ibid, TCN3 520, 529 – sale of works to Beardmore 1904, 1905. The agreement of sale was
     concluded in December 1905 with the understanding that Beardmore would acquire the works
     no later than Whitsunday 1907. The Works were sold to the Dalmuir Dry Dock Company Ltd
     which was set up in 1907 to manage the proposed dock.
8   Minutes of the Beardmore Company, June 1902 – also refers to the purchase of eight acres of land
     at Craigton – a district in the south of Glasgow (for the erection of gun factory). The *Clydebank
     Press* 9 October 1903 mentions a vacant site known as Brickfield on the Craigton Road to be
     developed by Vickers as a gun and locomotive works. The land surrounding the Clyde Trust
     Workshops appears to have been bought by John Hatt Noble Graham in 1900 – shortly before
     Beardmore. (Title deeds of ground at Dalmuir held by the Scottish Development Agency).
9   *Clydebank Press*, 29 February 1904 p6 .
10   Appendix to Petitions, The County Council of Dunbarton, November 1901, p 22 and 23 report
     by George Ross, Burgh Surveyor.
11   *Clydebank Press*, 23 November 1900 p8 .
12   Appendix to Petitions, The County Council of Dunbarton, November 1901, p 22 and 23 report
     by George Ross, Burgh Surveyor.
13   *Clydebank Press*, 13 September 1901 p5 James Goldie & Son also built Napier & Miller's
     shipyard at Old Kilpatrick.
14   *Clydebank Press*, 6 September 1901 p4.
15   Ibid, 29 June 1900 p5; 24 August 1900 p5; 2 May 1902 p4.
16   Register of Plans, Building Control Clydebank District Council.. See Appendix 10 for additional
     information. The costs are those recorded in the Profit & Loss accounts of William Beardmore
     & Co Ltd and indicate the amounts spent up to and including part of 1904 with the exception
     of the gantry which is up to and including part of 1905. To give an approximate idea of current
     purchasing power, multiply by 50.
17   *Engineering*, 7 October 1904 p455 and 2 February 1906 p140 for a general works description.
     Descriptions of the shipyard printed in technical publications during 1904 before the shipyard
     was complete, credit the yard with several major facilities, which although proposed, were never
     built. These include the 1,000 foot long graving dock; a glazed roof over the shipbuilding gantry,

two 850 foot long timber storage sheds and a coffer dam running the length of the berths at the water's edge which would have permitted working at the stern of a vessel on the stocks irrespective of the state of the tide.

18   *Clydebank Press*, 30 December 1904 p5.

19   UGD 100 1/8/7 Statement of Accounts of the Beardmore Company, 1 August 1907.

20   The valuation role for 1920 records these as Gilford House (George Langlands, Manager), Ravenswood (Alexander Galbraith, Shipyard Manager), The Tower (William Onyon, Engineering Manager) and Melbourne House (AJ Campbell, General Manager).

21   *Engineering* 7 October 1904 p455 and on articles about plant and facilities at Dalmuir shipyard which appear in *Engineering* throughout 1906.

22   The crane was ordered in June 1902 (*Clydebank Press* 20 June 1902 p5).

23   UGD 100 1/1/3 Minutes of the Beardmore Company, 19 January 1903 (hammerhead crane). Articles of Association of the Glasgow Crane & Electric Hoist Co Ltd.

24   Siegfried Herzog, *Elektrisch betriebene Krane und Aufzüge* Verlag von Albert Raustein. Zürich, 1905. A technical description of the crane.

25   *Engineering*, 5 January 1906 p5

26   *Engineering*, 20 March 1908 p359

27   Patents, dated 25 February 1904, applying to this gantry were taken out by GE Moore of Uddingston Glasgow and the Glasgow Electric Crane and Hoist Co Ltd of Parkhead, Engineering 1905 p491.

28   *Engineer*, 1905 p32.

29   *Clydebank Press*, 31 January 1908 p5. and 14 February 1908 p5.

30   The Dalmuir Dry Dock Company was not wound up until 1924. As if to keep the land available, no major buildings were ever erected on that part of the shipyard – William Beardmore did not give up on ideas easily!

31   Salaries Books of the Beardmore Company, 1921.

A HESITANT START: 1904 – 1909

1   The yard was unsuccessfully put up for sale twice. In 1910 the London and Glasgow Shipbuilding Company purchased over nine acres of the yard to build a fitting-out basin. That basin together with two adjacent yards were incorporated into one yard by Harland & Wolff in 1913.

2   The other yards were: Thames Iron Works, Cammell Laird, Palmers, Armstrong, Fairfield, John Brown and Scotts. Notes within the Ships Cover state that piling on the main berth had been completed with the exception of eighty feet and that the drawing provided by the Company showing the arrangement of the berths was generally satisfactory. The note went on to state that Beardmore hoped to have the graving dock built to accommodate the battleship on completion in 33 months time.

3   A small paragraph in *Engineering* states 'We have been requested by Messrs Beardmore to contradict statements made about the suspension of the *Agamemnon* because of subsidence of the building ways. This statement and another concerning changes within the Company's staff have been contradicted by the Beardmore solicitors Mitchells Johnson and Co.' *Engineering* 15 December 1905 p809.

4   *Engineering*, 12 October 1906 p502 and 22 March 1907 p388.

5   *Clydebank Press*, 29 June 1906 p8.

6   From an untitled newspaper article entitled Naval Scare kept in a book of clippings by the Duke of Montrose.

7   *Clydebank Press*, 28 August 1908 p7.

8   Ibid, 3 May 1907 p5.

9   *Engineering*, 12 February 1909 p209.

10   Ibid, 23 August 1907 p279 and 30 August 1907 p303

11   *Clydebank Press*, 20 December 1907 p5 and The Works of Wm Beardmore & Co Ltd, 1913

12   Correspondence between The Marquis of Graham and Trevor Dawson held by the Duke of Montrose.

13   *Clydebank Press*, 4 December 1908 p3.

14   Ibid, 6 April 1906 p2.

15   Ibid, 27 March 1908 p5.

16   *Engineering*, 25 September 1908 p422.

17   Ibid, 8 January 1909 p52.

18   Minutes of the Beardmore Company, 17 September 1908. The cost of John Brown's first destroyer was £110,954 and Fairfield's £107,884 (EJ March).

19   *Engineering*, 13 April 1906 p502 and p478.

20   Ibid, 3 July 1908 p15 and 2 October 1908 p450.

21   The Duke of Montrose. My *Ditty Box* p149 and 150.

22   Hume & Moss, *Beardmore: The History of a Scottish Industrial Giant*, p78.

23   Annual accounts of the Beardmore Company, 1 August 1910.

24   *Clydebank Press*, 17 September 1909 p2.

25   From an untitled newspaper article entitled Naval Scare kept in a book of clippings by the Duke of Montrose. The statement continued '... The Agamemnon, the last battleship built by us, took 37 months to build and complete, but her progress was greatly delayed by continued alterations in her design after the ship was begun, and owing to subsidiary contractors not receiving sufficient notice for the order of their special manufactures. The way to expedite shipbuilding is to have a regular progressive naval policy from year to year, so that shipbuilders and contractors can arrange their plant and their orders to ensure a regular supply in good time of the component parts of the ship'.

26   *Clydebank Press*, 26 March 1909 p2.

STEADY PROGRESS: 1910 – 1913

1   *Engineering*, 3 June 1910 p.714.

2   *Glasgow Herald*, 21 October 1910 p13.

3   *Clydebank Press*, 10 June 1910 p4.

4   Ibid, 5 May 1911 p3.

5   *Glasgow Herald* Trade Review, 1910 p25 and 1911 p25 .

6   Ibid. also Engineering, 9 September 1910 p.376.

7   *Brasseys Naval Annual* 1911, p320.

8   *Glasgow Herald* Trade Review, 1908 p38.

9   *Glasgow Herald* Trade Review, 1911 p32.

10   *Shipbuilding & Shipping Record*, 20 November 1913, p664.

11   Ibid, 19 March 1914, p366.

THE GREAT WAR: 1914 – 1918

1   Public Record Office, ADM 116 – 1583 Shipyard Labour Department 1917-18.

2   Raven A, Roberts J. *British Battleships of World War 2*, p51.

3   *Glasgow Herald* Trade Review 1915 p33.

4   HMS Ramillies Ships Cover, National Maritime Museum.

5   *Warship*, Volume 36 October 1985 p248 article by RA Burt on Royal Sovereign Class battleships. The Beardmore Company publication *Romance of Engineering* states that the Ramillies was the heaviest ship for her length so far launched.

6   King-Hall S. A *North Sea Diary*, p183 onwards for a full account of the difficult passage of the Ramillies down the Clyde.

7   HMS Argus Ships Cover, National Maritime Museum.

8   Ibid.

9   Correspondence between The Duke of Montrose and The Royal Commission on Awards to Inventors held by the Duke of Montrose.

10 Ibid.

11 Public Records Office, Record of Naval Construction 1914-18. Adm 1/8547/340.

12 Ibid.

13 *Wm Beardmore & Co Ltd* reprinted from *Empire Illustrated* 1919.

14 Fairfield had one berth occupied for two years by a sister ship of the battlecruiser Hood which was laid down on 9 October 1916, suspended on 9 March 1917 and finally cancelled in October 1918.

15 Tennyson D'Eyncourt, Sir E H W. A *Shipbuilders Yarn*, p69

16 *The Shipbuilder*, 1921 p244.

17 *Glasgow Herald*, 28 December 1918 p8.

18 *The Shipbuilder*, 1919 p34.

19 *Engineering*, 25 August 1916 p175 and 17 November 1916 p486.

20 The other firms were Stephen, Denny, Barclay Curle, Napier & Miller and Fairfield.

21 *Beardmore News*, August 1926 p108.

22 The Aviation Department was initially managed by R S Hubbard who left in February 1916 to join Handley Page.

23 King, HF. *Sopwith Aircraft 1912-20*, p129.

24 PRO MUN 5/164/1124/36.

25 *Wm Beardmore & Co Ltd* reprinted from *Empire Illustrated* 1919.

26 Jellicoe, *The Grand Fleet 1914-16*, p453.

27 PRO AIR 11/181 XC/A50714.

28 At least some of these buildings were built by Leslie Kirk, Kilbowie Road, Clydebank. (From County of Renfrew Second District, Register of New Buildings)

29 Ibid also PRO AIR 11/181 XC/A50714.

30 Information concerning the airship shed taken from the drawings held by Sir Wm Arrol & Co Ltd.

31 *Wm Beardmore & Co Ltd* reprinted from *Empire Illustrated* 1919.

32 Scott & Cunnison, *Economic & Social History of the World War; Clyde Valley Industries* p168.

33 Dalmuir & West of Scotland Estates Ltd, Minute Book UGD 100 2/1/1.

34 *Clydebank Press*, 26 May 1916 p5.

35 Interview with Findlay Hart, an apprentice plumber at the yard at the end of World War 1.

36 *Beardmore News*, June 1921 p2 and *Shipbuilding & Shipping Record* 28 August 1919 p246.

THE POST WAR BOOM AND AFTER: 1919 – 1923

1   Wm Beardmore & Co Ltd, *Romance of Engineering*, 1926.

2   *Shipbuilding & Shipping Record*, 4 September 1919 p269.

3   *Beardmore News*, July 1920 p5.

4   Profit & Loss accounts of the Beardmore Company 1 August 1921.

5   Accounts of the Beardmore Company 18 February 1920.

6   The Fairfield yard, which was largely concentrated to the east of the fitting out basin, was equipped with four very expensive new berths to the west of the basin. Two of these berths were completely covered and the other two were served by a large gantry designed and erected by Redpath Brown.

7   *Beardmore News*, November 1923 p3.

8   Ibid, April 1920 p37.

9   *Engineer* 13 August 1920 p148.

10 PRO MUN 5/164/1124/36.

11 *Flight*, 22 July 1922; Jackson, AJ, *British Civil Aircraft Since 1919* Volume 1 p298.

12 Ibid, 2 September 1920 p948.

13   *Glasgow Herald*, 17 February 1919 p8 and 7.
14   *Flight*, 27 March 1919 p417.
15   *Glasgow Herald*, 25 April 1919 p8.
16   *Flight* 4 December 1919 p1548 and 22 June 1920 p90.
17   *Flight* 31 July 1919 p1020.
18   PRO AIR 11/194/5303; *Engineering* 25 March 1921 p454.
19   *Glasgow Herald*, 17 April 1923 p8. and 25 May 1923 p7.
20   Minutes of the Beardmore Company, 18 February 1920.
21   *Engineering*, 28 January 1927 p102.
22   *Shipbuilding & Shipping Record*, 27 May 1920 p706.
23   *Beardmore News*, January 1920 p2.
24   *Engineering*, 26 August 1921 p315.
25   *Glasgow Herald*, 21 June 1921 p9.
26   *Beardmore News*, January 1922 p4.
27   *Glasgow Herald*, 12 April 1922 p12.
28   *Engineering*, 4 May 1923 p551 and 30 November 1923 p679.
29   *Beardmore News*, January 1922 p4.
30   Raven A & Roberts J, *British Battleships of World War 2*, p98.
31   1921 Battlecruiser Ships Cover, National Maritime Museum.
32   *Beardmore News*, January 1922 p4.
33   *Engineer*, 5 January 1923, p1.
34   *Shipbuilding & Shipping Record*, 20 July 1922 p92.
35   *Clydebank Press*, 12 Oct 1923 p5.
36   *The Shipbuilder*, 1923 p244
37   Richardsons Westgarth & Co Ltd, acquired a license to build Beardmore Tosi diesels. They engined two vessels, *Sycamore* and *Tramore* built on the Tees during 1924, with Beardmore diesels.

THE FINAL YEARS: 1924 – 1930

1   *Flight*, 29 May 1924 p307.
2   'The Beardmore Monoplane' a brochure held by the Royal Scottish Museum, Edinburgh.
3   *Flight*, 26 February 1925 p122, 31 December 1925 p850 and 25 February 1926 p111.
4   Ibid, 26 February 1925 p122.
5   Ibid, 17 July 1924 p449.
6   *Engineer*, 27 March 1929 p350.
7   *Flight*, 11 March 1926 p152.
8   Ibid, 10 November 1927 p778; 12 January 1928 p21; 8 March 1928 p163; 5 July 1928 p5 (supplement). Also *British Civil Aircraft Since 1919*, p331.
9   *Engineer*, 23 August 1929 p206
10   March EJ, *British Destroyers 1892-1953*, Seely Service 1970 p261
11   *Shipbuilding & Shipping Record*, 2 July 1925 p1.
12   *Shipbuilding & Shipping Record*, 8 Oct 1925 p369.
13   *Glasgow Herald*, 30 June 1925 p11.
14   *Engineering*, 6 November 1925 p575.
15   *Shipbuilding & Shipping Record*, 15 July 1926 p77.
16   Minutes of the Beardmore Company, 19 February 1929. Galbraith left this position in 1929 following a dispute concerning bonuses for Atholl Steel Houses.
17   Minutes of the Beardmore Company, 1 March 1928.
18   *Glasgow Herald*, 15 September 1927 p12.
19   Ibid, 3 November 1927 p10 and 12.
20   Hume JR and Moss MS, *Beardmore: The History of a Scottish Industrial Giant*, Heinemann 1979

– offers an insight into the affairs of the Beardmore Company including a very detailed account of the various schemes to restructure the company

21   *Glasgow Herald*, 31 March 1927 p9.

22   *The Shipbuilder*, November 1928 p683.

23   Hume JR and Moss MS, *Beardmore: The History of a Scottish Industrial Giant*, Heinemann 1979 p204.

24   *Glasgow Herald*, 22 September 1924 p10.

25   *Engineering*, 20 November 1925 p647.

26   *The Locomotive*, 15 November 1927, p349

27   *Engineering*, 20 May 1927 p608 and 24 June 1927 p760

28   *Shipbuilding & Shipping Record*, 8 August 1929

29   *Shipbuilding & Shipping Record*, 3 October 1929 p411

30   *Shipbuilding & Shipping Record*, 1 August 1929

31   Ibid, p147

32   *Shipbuilding & Shipping Record*, 20 March 1930 p366

33   Napier & Miller, Old Kilpatrick; Archibald McMillan, Dumbarton; Harland & Wolff, Greenock, (formerly Cairds); Bow McLachlan, Paisley

34   Glasgow University Archives, UCS 1/22/31- John Brown file regarding Dalmuir

35   *Glasgow Herald*, 28 October 1930 p10

36   From Shirlaw Allan's sale catalogue.

37   Minutes of the Beardmore Company, 8 December 1930

38   Hume JR and Moss MS, *Beardmore: The History of a Scottish Industrial Giant*, Heinemann 1979 p218

39   Ibid p.234 and 235

40   Title deeds of ground at Dalmuir held by the Scottish Development Agency (1982)

41   Ibid

42   Ibid

BIBLIOGRAPHY

BOOKS

Arrol Sir William & Co. Bridges, Structural Steelwork and Mechanical Engineering Productions. London, 1909

BARNES CH. *Handley Page Aircraft Since 1907.* Putnam, 1976

BROWN DK, *The Design of Aircraft Carriers Prior to WW2.* Interdisciplinary Science Reviews Vol 8, No 4, 1983

BRUCE J M, *British Aeroplanes 1914-18.* Putnam, 1957

BURT RA, *British Battleships of World War One.* Arms & Armour Press, 1987

CONNON P, *An Aeronautical History of the Cumbria, Dumfries and Galloway Region Part 2.* St Patrick's Press, Penrith 1984

Conway's All The Worlds Fighting Ships 1906-1921. Conway Maritime Press, 1985

Conway's All The Worlds Fighting Ships 1922-1946. Conway Maritime Press, 1980

DIMITRIEV NI & KOLLICHEV VV. *Shipbuilding Works and Shipbuilding in Russia and Abroad,* St Petersburg, 1909

DITTMAR F J & COLLEDGE J J. *British Warships 1914-18.* Ian Allan 1972

FRIEDMAN N. *British Carrier Aviation,* Conway 1988

GILLIES JD & WOOD JL. *Aviation in Scotland.* Royal Aeronautical Society 1966

GRAHAM J, 6TH DUKE OF MONTROSE. *My Ditty Box,* Cape, 1952

HERZOG S. *Elektrisch betriebene Krane und Afzüge.* Verlag von Albert Raustein, Zürich 1905

HIGHAM R. *The British Rigid Airship 1908-1931.* GT Foulis 1961

HORNBY W. *History of the Second World War Factories and Plant.* HMSO, 1958

HUME JR & MOSS MS. *Beardmore; the history of a Scottish industrial giant.* Heinemann 1979

JACKSON AJ. *British Civil Aircraft Since 1919* Vol 1. Putnam, 1973

JELLICOE ADMIRAL LORD. *The Grand Fleet 1914-16: Its Creation, Development and Work.* Cassell, 1919

KING-HALL S. *A North Sea Diary.* Newnes, 1919

KING HF. *Sopwith Aircraft 1912-1920.* Putnam, 1981

KLUDAS A. *Great Passenger Ships of the World,* Vol 1, 2 and 3. Patrick Stephens Limited, 1975

LAYMAN RD. *Before The Aircraft Carrier,* Conway, 1989

LIPSCOMBE FW. *The British Submarine,* Conway, 1975

LOWE JW. *British Steam Locomotive Builders.* Goose and Sons, 1975

MACLEOD. *Clyde District of Dumbartonshire.* Dumbarton,1886

MARCH EJ. *British Destroyers 1892-1953.* Seeley Service & Co Ltd 1970

MARDER A. *From Dreadnought to Scapa Flow, Vol 1 The Road to War.* Oxford, 1961-70

NOEL-BAKER P. *The Private Manufacture of Armaments.* Gollancz, 1936

PADFIELD P. *The Great Naval Race.* 1974

PARKINSON JR. *The Economics of Shipbuilding in the United Kingdom,* Cambridge, 1960

PATERSON A T. *Jellicoe. A Biography.* Macmillan, 1969 PEEBLES H. *Warshipbuilding on the Clyde.* John Donald. 1987

POLLARD S & ROBERTSON P. *The British Shipbuilding Industry 1870-1914.* Harvard University Press, 1979

RAVEN A & ROBERTS J. *British Battleships of World War 2.* Arms & Armour Press, 1979

RANFT B. *Technical Change and British Naval Policy 1860-1939.* Hodder & Stoughton, 1977

ROSKILL SW. *British Naval Policy Between the Wars.* Collins, 1968-76

SCOTT & CUNNISON. *The Industries of the Clyde Valley during the War*, Clarendon Press, 1924

SCOTT JD. *Vickers: A History*. Weidenfeld & Nicolson, 1962

SMITH EC. *A Short History of Naval and Marine Engineering*. Cambridge University Press 1937

STURTIVANT R & PAGE G. *Royal Navy Serials and Units 1911-1919*. Air-Britain Ltd, 1992

TENNYSON D'EYNCOURT EHW. *A Shipbuilders Yarn*. Hutchison, 1947

VENTRY A F D & KOLESNIK E M. *Airship Saga*. Blanford Press, 1982

WARREN K. *Armstrongs of Elswick*. Macmillan, 1989

NEWSPAPERS AND PERIODICALS

The Clydebank Press 1900-30

The Engineer 1900-30

Engineering 1900-30

Flight 1919-30

The Glasgow Herald 1900-30

The Locomotive 1920-30

The Shipbuilder 1906-30

Shipbuilding & Shipping Record 1913-30

Warren (Volumes 1-49 Conway Maritime Press 1977-88)

RECORDS

The records of William Beardmore and Company Limited held at Glasgow University Archives:

Minute Books UGD 100 1/1/1 to 1/1/4

Agenda Books UGD 100 1/2/1 to 1/2/4

Statement of Accounts UGD 100 1/8/1 to 1/8/30

Salaries Books UGD 100 1/9/1 to 1/9/4

Dalmuir & West of Scotland Estates Ltd, Minute Books UGD 100/2/1/1 to 2/1/3

Wm Beardmore & Co Ltd, The Romance of Engineering, 1926

Wm Beardmore & Co Ltd, The Works of William Beardmore & Co Ltd, – reprinted from
        Engineering 1910

Wm Beardmore & Co Ltd, The Works of William Beardmore & Co Ltd – reprinted from
        Empire Illustrated 1913

INDEX